GW00566657

# Durham Rocks

**50** extraordinary rocky places that tell the story of the Durham landscape

Ian Jackson

First published in the United Kingdom in 2023 by Northern Heritage Services Limited

Units 7&8 New Kennels, Blagdon Estate, Seaton Burn, Newcastle upon Tyne NE13 6DB

Telephone: 01670 789 940          www.northern-heritage.co.uk

See www.northern-heritage.co.uk for full catalogue

Text copyright: © 2023 Ian Jackson

Edited by Abigail Burt, Angus Lunn and Tony Cousins

Photographs not otherwise attributed: © 2023 Ian Jackson

Design and layout: © 2023 Ian Jackson

Graphic design: Ian Jackson and Abigail Burt

Mapping contains data from OS ©Crown copyright and database right (2023)
and ©OpenStreetMap contributors, Openstreetmap.org/copyright.

Printed and bound in the UK by W & G Baird

British Library Cataloguing in Publishing Data

A catalogue record for this book is available from the British Library.

ISBN 9781916237698

All rights reserved.

No part of this book may be reproduced, stored or introduced into a retrieval system,
or transmitted in any form or by any means (electronic, mechanical, photocopying,
recording or otherwise) without the publisher's prior permission.

**Durham**
Wildlife Trust
**From Tees to Tyne**

NORTHERN
HERITAGE

WORLD
LAND
TRUST™

www.carbonbalancedpaper.com
CBP002879

FSC
www.fsc.org
MIX
Paper | Supporting
responsible forestry
FSC® C016201

# Iain Stewart

*For its size Durham packs a huge geological punch. The rocks that form its dramatic coastline and underpin the Pennine hills and valleys are world class and world famous. Just like Ian's two other northern Rock books, Durham Rocks does something I'm passionate about, it makes good science attractive, accessible and relevant to everyone. The fascinating stories told in plain words and the wonderful images connect you with the bones of the landscape and with its wildlife, history, culture and economy. Explore the Durham beneath your feet and you'll discover what makes this small county special in so many ways.*

**Professor Iain Stewart MBE** is a geologist who has presented many BBC documentaries on the history and dynamics of the Earth. His passion is to improve the communication of science. He is currently Jordan-UK El Hassan bin Talal Research Chair in Sustainability.

Grindstone Sill, Carr Crags, above Bowlees
(Cover image: Chemical Beach, Seaham)

# Foreword

**Durham**
Wildlife Trust
**From Tees to Tyne**

We are incredibly fortunate to have an amazing diversity of wildlife in the region that Durham Wildlife Trust protects. Our landscapes range from high Pennine hills and valleys, each with their unique flora, to rugged coastal cliffs and limestone grasslands of international importance.

The foundation for this biodiversity is our geodiversity: the wonderful variety of rocks that underpin it all. But these rocks are also the basis for so much more of Durham's character; its history, economy and culture.

Because it has such a fundamental role in conserving and protecting habitats and wildlife, Durham Wildlife Trust regards geology as a key element of its mission. Through our reserves and work programmes we seek to promote a greater awareness and understanding of geology in our county.

We are delighted to have this book as the latest contribution to that goal. Its beautiful images and straightforward language describe 50 special places across our county. They will surely help you appreciate the relevance of the rocks beneath our feet to our environment today and to its conservation in the future.

*Jim Cokill*

*Director Durham Wildlife Trust*

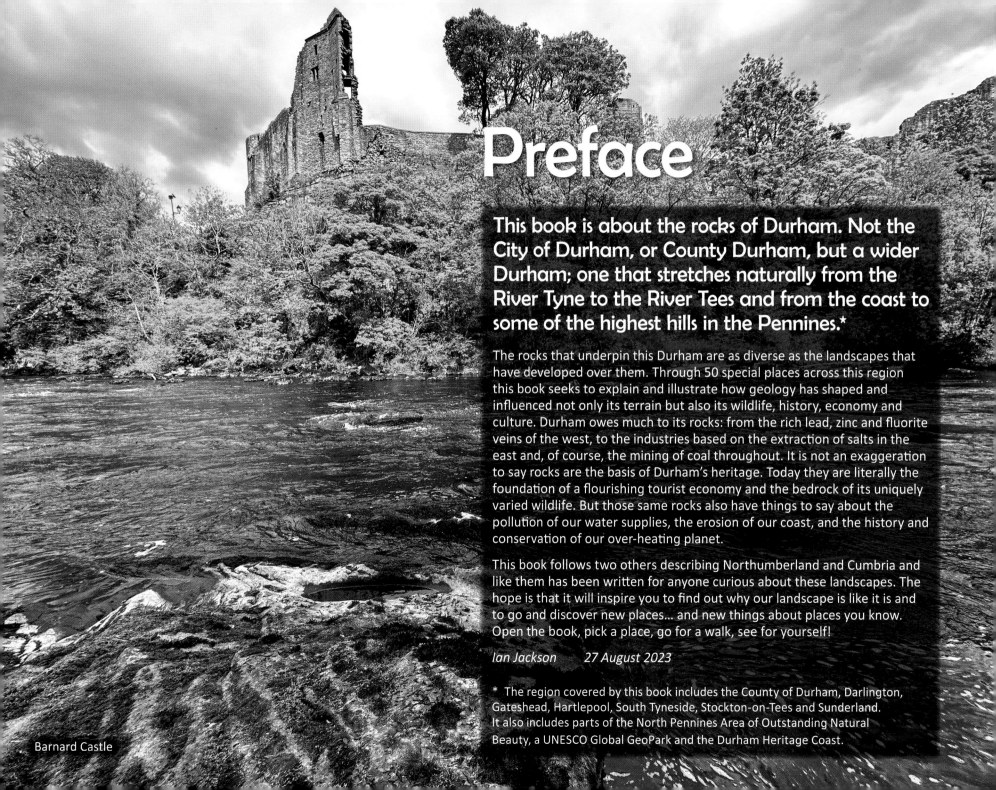

# Preface

This book is about the rocks of Durham. Not the City of Durham, or County Durham, but a wider Durham; one that stretches naturally from the River Tyne to the River Tees and from the coast to some of the highest hills in the Pennines.*

The rocks that underpin this Durham are as diverse as the landscapes that have developed over them. Through 50 special places across this region this book seeks to explain and illustrate how geology has shaped and influenced not only its terrain but also its wildlife, history, economy and culture. Durham owes much to its rocks: from the rich lead, zinc and fluorite veins of the west, to the industries based on the extraction of salts in the east and, of course, the mining of coal throughout. It is not an exaggeration to say rocks are the basis of Durham's heritage. Today they are literally the foundation of a flourishing tourist economy and the bedrock of its uniquely varied wildlife. But those same rocks also have things to say about the pollution of our water supplies, the erosion of our coast, and the history and conservation of our over-heating planet.

This book follows two others describing Northumberland and Cumbria and like them has been written for anyone curious about these landscapes. The hope is that it will inspire you to find out why our landscape is like it is and to go and discover new places... and new things about places you know. Open the book, pick a place, go for a walk, see for yourself!

*Ian Jackson        27 August 2023*

* The region covered by this book includes the County of Durham, Darlington, Gateshead, Hartlepool, South Tyneside, Stockton-on-Tees and Sunderland. It also includes parts of the North Pennines Area of Outstanding Natural Beauty, a UNESCO Global GeoPark and the Durham Heritage Coast.

Barnard Castle

# Sources and acknowledgements

The maps, memoirs and reports produced by field geologists of the British Geological Survey are the main sources of information for this book. I want to thank former colleagues and friends for the enormous wealth of practical geoscience they delivered across the whole of the country.

I would especially like to thank Brian Young, Tony Cooper and Geoff Kimbell for being so willing to share their unrivalled expertise. In preparing this book hundreds of scientific papers, books, articles and fieldtrip guides were also read and I thank their authors. It is impossible to name them all but the research carried out by scientists of the University of Durham and the Yorkshire Geological Society has been invaluable. Google, Wikipedia and many other web sites were searched to seek out information on the historical and cultural connections. Neither the local authorities nor the North Pennines Area of Outstanding Natural Beauty have the resources today to employ in-house geological expertise but I am extremely grateful for the work done by them in the past, in particular Elizabeth Pickett, and by their ecologists and external consultants today.

I would like to pay tribute to Chris Hartnell of Northern Heritage Services, who has had the courage to publish three books about rocks when all his business-sense must have cautioned him otherwise.

Angus Lunn again took on the challenge of providing information on the flora and fauna of several sites and Abigail Burt turned a mock-up of the book prepared in PowerPoint into the professional piece of graphic design you see now. Angus and Abigail together with Tony Cousins kindly read and commented on drafts of the book, but any errors in the book are mine.

Thank you to my wife, Gill and walking friends for accompanying me on hikes that always seemed to involve an off-the-beaten-track rocky location. As with previous books, most of the photographs were taken with my iPhone. Author's royalties after printing costs will be donated to Durham Wildlife Trust.

God's Bridge: a natural limestone bridge over the River Greta near Bowes

# Introduction

Durham's rocks* define its landscapes. From the remote heather moors and dales of the Pennine hills in the west, to the pastures, towns and villages of the east, as lower ground meets the coastal plain. All owe their character to the underlying geology.

Sparsely populated rural uplands on older Carboniferous rocks give way eastwards to old mining and post-industrial settlements on younger Carboniferous and Permian rocks, settlements which are, metaphorically if not literally, built on coal. These broad divisions of landscape each have multiple facets which reflect the detail of the rocks beneath them. These stones tell stories about Durham's past environments; from tropical swamps and coral reefs to rocky deserts and desiccated seas and, less than 20,000 years ago, to a frozen wasteland.

The tales do not end there. Since the time of Mesolithic hunters and gatherers, perhaps 10,000 years ago, we have exploited these rocks, for stone axes, coal, lead, limestone, salt and water supply and today for tourism and recreation. Bishops, mineowners and politicians have exercised power through the huge wealth that rocks have generated but the demise of the industries based on these natural resources has seen communities fight to survive.

Geology defines Durham. Perhaps less well known is that in a sense Durham defined geology. Back in the 14th Century a Durham bishop, Richard de Bury, seeking to untangle the philosophical distinctions between law, art and science invented the term 'geologia' – Earthly science. It was not the last time this small English county would influence geology across the world.

To tell the story and make those connections the 50 sites have been divided into five themes although many sites could easily fit into several themes.

*Some will argue, not unreasonably, that several sites in this book are hardly rocks. True, but collectively the 50 sites tell the full story of Durham's landscape and set in context the brief narrative of humankind.*

The tomb of Bishop Richard de Bury, in Durham Cathedral

## Ancient rivers, seas & life

1 Blast Beach, Seaham
2 Claxheugh Rock
3 Cronkley
4 Falcon Clints
5 Harehope Quarry
6 Hell Kettles
7 Hown's Gill
8 Little Scar and Long Scar
9 Middridge Quarry
10 North Grain
11 Pallis Burn
12 Roker
13 Tunstall Hills

## Volcanoes & molten rock

14 Cockfield
15 High Force
16 Holwick Scars
17 Rookhope
18 Stanhope
19 Widdybank Fell

## Earthquakes & folded rocks

20 Burtreeford
21 Butterknowle
22 Houghton-le-Spring
23 Marsden Bay
24 Middlehope Burn
25 Salterfen Point

## Climate & landscape change

26 Burnhope Seat
27 Chopwell Woods
28 Coldberry Gutter
29 Easington Colliery
30 Goldsborough
31 Hartlepool Bay
32 Moking Hurth Cave
33 Penshaw & Worm Hills
34 Piercebridge
35 Ryhope cliffs
36 Team Valley
37 Warren House Gill

## Heritage & mining

38 Barningham
39 Blaydon Bank Quarry
40 Blaydon Burn
41 Consett
42 Dinsdale
43 Durham Cathedral
44 Durham Mining Museum
45 Felling
46 Groverake Mine
47 Killhope
48 Saltholme
49 South Shields
50 Stony Heap

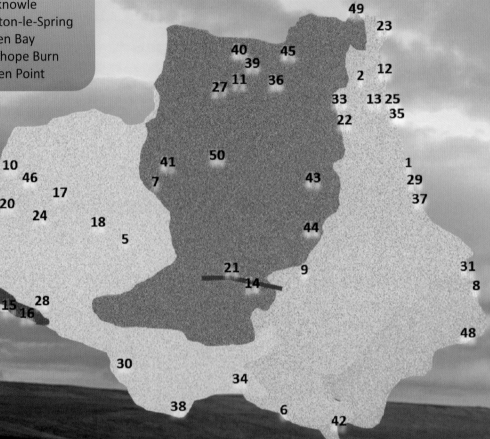

# 50 sites in 5 themes

County boundary on the Alston-Teesdale road

# Durham's geological journey

Our geological journey begins at the bottom of a deep ocean as we move away from the South Pole. Mud and sand fill the ocean and the tectonic plates carrying the continents collide, forcing one deep beneath the other.

Kilometres deep in the Earth's crust molten magma filled huge chambers which slowly cooled and solidified.

Sea level rose and fell frequently as the Earth's ice caps grew and receded as sandy deltas and peaty swamps were repeatedly inundated by warm coral seas.

The crust beneath us was being stretched; molten magma and hot mineral rich fluids exploited the cracks.

Seas teeming with life covered all of northern England, but the rocks they left behind have all been eroded away.

Lava started to pour out of an enormous rift that was to split continents and become the Atlantic Ocean. North America and Europe have been drifting apart ever since.

millions of years ago

| 485 | 444 | 360 | 359 | 299 | 252 | 201 | 2.6 | 0 |

Ordovician

Silurian to Devonian

Early Carboniferous rocks

Carboniferous Coal Measures

Permian

Triassic

Jurassic, Cretaceous and younger rocks

Ice Ages

Weardale Granite

Whin Sill

Cleveland-Armathwaite Dyke

Sediments continued to fill the ocean and forces within the Earth that had sutured the continents together then buckled the crust into a huge mountain chain. In Durham there is no record in the rocks of these times.

Millions of years of erosion wore those mountains down and huge rivers brought down billions of tons of sand and mud. By now the tectonic plate on which Britain lay had reached the Equator and our environment had become tropical.

We drifted north into arid latitudes and sand dunes blew across a rocky desert. Sea level rose again and Durham lay on the western coast of an evaporating, limey salty sea with barrier reefs.

Transient and flood-prone rivers deposited even more red sand and silt on a red hot plain.

2.6 million years ago in the Quaternary period Earth's temperature began to fluctuate again, we cooled and then warmed, repeatedly. Polar ice caps extended to lower latitudes, glaciers grew and then retreated and as they did trees and plants re-colonised the landscape. Humans emerged and began to exert their influence on the area, clearing forests and settling in the valleys. But it is our impact on the planet in the last 200 years that far outstrips the previous 300,000 years of our existence.

COUNTY DURHAM
Land of the Prince Bishops

# Blast Beach, Seaham

**There are lots of fossils in Durham's rocks but finding places where you can safely see or collect these fossils can be a challenge.**

One of the places to hunt them out is Blast Beach just south of Seaham, but it's not the natural Permian limestone bedrock in the cliff that is the source of most of these fossils, it's the eroding waste from coal mines and iron-making that is at the base of the cliff and on the foreshore. This waste contains a lot of Carboniferous shale and sandstone. These rocks are around 315 million years old and were once mud and sand in tropical lagoons and rivers, beside which grew primitive plants and trees. Search through the boulders and pebbles on the beach and you can find scaley patterns and leaves on stones; some of these are from giant club mosses. In the mix of Carboniferous and Permian rocks you might see bryozoans and corals, once part of reefs, as well as shells and ironstone nodules.

Fossils are not the only things to look out for on the beach, we humans are adding our own chapter to the geological story. The layer of waste at the base of the cliff is obvious: coal dust, bricks and iron slag from long gone blast furnaces on the cliff top. On the foreshore are flint pebbles, once ballast from returning coal ships; polished glass from a nearby former bottle works; and even alien igneous rocks, pieces of the giant blocks of larvikite rock imported from Norway to protect the coastline. If it is fossils you're after, Blast Beach isn't the only place to see them. Look for them on all of the Durham beaches, or search the shingle banks of rivers that bring down fossils in Carboniferous rocks. Then there are the museums in Sunderland and Newcastle - perfect for cold rainy days. But there's no substitute for being outdoors and discovering something that was living more than 300 million years ago!

Take the path from the cliff top car park down onto the beach [NZ438477]

Fossils and pebbles on Blast Beach

# Claxheugh Rock

**This riverside cliff starts at the bottom with rocks that used to be desert sands and finishes at the top with ones that were once coral reefs. What happened?**

Around 300 million years ago our climate changed; what is now Britain and northern Europe had drifted north away from the Equator. A landscape of tropical swamps and lazy rivers became a hot and arid rocky plain, one of the Earth's biggest ever deserts. Over almost 50 million years more than 500 metres of rocks were eroded away. You can see the evidence of that desert weathering in the red-purple colour of those older Carboniferous rocks at Castletown just above the river on the north bank. On this rocky plain sand was deposited, blown by the wind into long dune ridges. The dunes can be up to 70 metres high and two kilometres across, but in between them there may be little or no sand at all. These massive dunes are now the yellow sandstone rock in the cliff and their sloping layers and wind frosted round quartz grains are evidence of their desert dune origin. The sandstone grains are only held together with iron minerals, so they are soft and friable and weather quickly to become sand again. Although they have been used for building sand, the Permian Yellow Sands (the name that geologists give them) are relevant to us because underground they contain huge amounts of water; they are an important aquifer. This water caused serious problems for coal miners as they dug shafts and boreholes to reach the coal seams beneath. The solutions were pumping the water out of the ground, freezing the rocks to stop water reaching the workings or leaving wide rock barriers. All were expensive and meant that the operating lives of mines were reduced. These fossil sand dunes continue under the North Sea and their capacity to hold fluids means they are an important reservoir for oil and gas. It was research onshore by geologists in Durham that helped predict where those ancient dunes (and the oil and gas) would be.

The sharp divide between the Yellow Sands and the overlying grey Magnesian Limestone in the cliff at Claxheugh shows how desert conditions rapidly came to an end as a salty sea called the Zechstein flooded the land from Poland to England and coral reefs grew where sand dunes once were.

You can take the Metro to South Hylton; it's a 1 kilometre walk from there. Or park near the Rock beside the river [NZ363575]

Yellow Sands below Magnesian Limestone

# Cronkley

**Peeping through the Carboniferous strata in the valley of the River Tees beneath Cronkley Scar are the oldest rocks in Durham.**

These grey-green slates are part of the Skiddaw Group from the Ordovician period of Earth's history. Geologists know these rocks as the Teesdale Inlier, that's where older rocks are surrounded by younger ones. Primitive marine fossils, called graptolites, help us confirm the age of the slates at between 485 and 460 million years old. The rocks were once mud at the bottom of a deep ocean known as the Iapetus. That ocean was being squeezed between two continents and would ultimately cease to exist. Our part of Britain was near the South Pole then. Over millions of years, as our tectonic plate migrated north, the muds have been buried by thousands of metres of other sediments and heated by molten rocks beneath. Pressure and high temperatures have changed them and they became slate, a common metamorphic rock and one which splits readily.

Beside the small outcrop of these rocks is a stone ruin. It is the site of a mill which manufactured slate pencils in the 1850s. Slate pencils are so-called not because the pencils were made of slate, but because they were for writing on slate tablets, which Victorian children knew well. From the pieces of pencils still lying around it looks as if they have been produced by sawing the slates into square-sectioned rods. In this part of Teesdale the locals called these pencils Widdies after nearby Widdibank Fell. Just upstream there are some different and slightly younger Ordovician rocks called tuffs – ash ejected from a volcanic vent which has hardened into stone. This small outcrop is probably the same age and origin as the volcanic rocks of the central Lake District.

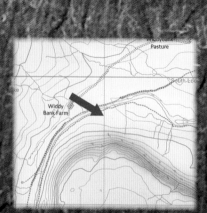

There is a car park in Forest-in-Teesdale. It's a 2 kilometre walk west over the River Tees from there [NY848295]

Ruins of slate pencil mill and outcrop of slate

# Falcon Clints

**The name must be literal. Clint from the Norse word meaning a rocky cliff and Falcon from the peregrines that occupy it still, or perhaps the golden eagles that once soared above it?**

Falcon Clints is in Upper Teesdale, just downstream from Cauldron Snout. The upper part of the cliff is made of the same Whin Sill dolerite that forms the waterfall of the Snout. Its characteristic vertical columns are very obvious - they were caused by the molten magma cooling, shrinking and cracking. The lower part of the cliff is marginally paler limestone (it has horizontal layers) that was altered to marble by heat caused by the injection of the Whin Sill's molten magma around 295 million years ago. But this description is not just about the Whin Sill and the limestone that became marble, it is about what lies beneath them at the very bottom of the cliff. At the east end of Falcon Clints, the Pennine Way footpath runs over a darker rubbly looking rock. It's from the earliest part of the Carboniferous period about 350 million years ago and it is called a conglomerate: a rock made of pebbles and cobbles in a matrix of mudstone. It is the product of millions of years of erosion of an ancient mountain chain when torrents of water carried, tumbled, and eventually deposited this mix of different-sized debris. Sea level then rose and many layers of limestone, plus sandstone and shale completely concealed the conglomerate. Millions more years of erosion and especially the work of the glaciers and rivers in the last 2.6 million years, has exposed this rock at the surface.

Whether you walk upstream or downstream to see Falcon Clints you have a great chance of spotting some special birds: dipper, lapwing and oystercatcher, maybe ring ouzel and blackcock, and if you are lucky, a peregrine falcon.

Park at Cow Green reservoir and walk 3 kilometres south. Take care passing Cauldron Snout [NY819282]

Conglomerate with pebbles of older rocks

Dolerite of the Whin Sill forms the top of the cliff and limestone layers appear below

# Harehope Quarry

**There are many different layers of limestone rock in northern England. One of the most widespread is known as the Great Limestone. Harehope Quarry and the bed of the Bollihope Burn in Weardale are good places to see it.**

In Northumberland, the Vale of Eden and north of the Lake District, the Great Limestone is around 15 metres thick; in the Durham Pennines it can exceed 30 metres. This limestone has very consistent and distinctive layers (beds) within it that can be recognised across our region; some beds are rich in characteristic fossils and have been given names. The Frosterley Marble, which is displayed beautifully in Bollihope Burn, is one of these beds and it is spectacular. It is full of the fossils of a coral called 'Dibunophyllum'. While not a true marble (that's a metamorphic rock that has been heated or subjected to intense pressure) it is so attractive when polished that it has been used as an ornamental stone in many famous buildings, including Durham and Mumbai cathedrals.

The coral fossils are a clue to what the environment was like when this limestone was formed around 330 million years ago. At that time in the Carboniferous period, Britain was almost on the Equator and was covered by shallow sub-tropical seas. It is the debris and fossils of billions of shells, corals and small animals made of calcium carbonate that make all limestones, including the chalk of the White Cliffs of Dover. Carboniferous limestone was once quarried here and all over Durham and it is usually dug in huge quantities to produce a flux for making iron and steel and for cement, roadstone and agricultural lime. But its use as a polished monumental stone is special. Today Harehope Quarry is a Local Wildlife Site which promotes biodiversity and geodiversity and encourages outdoor learning through educational visits and courses.

The quarry is southeast of Frosterley [NZ037363]

Fossils of corals in limestone in the dry bed of Bollihope Burn

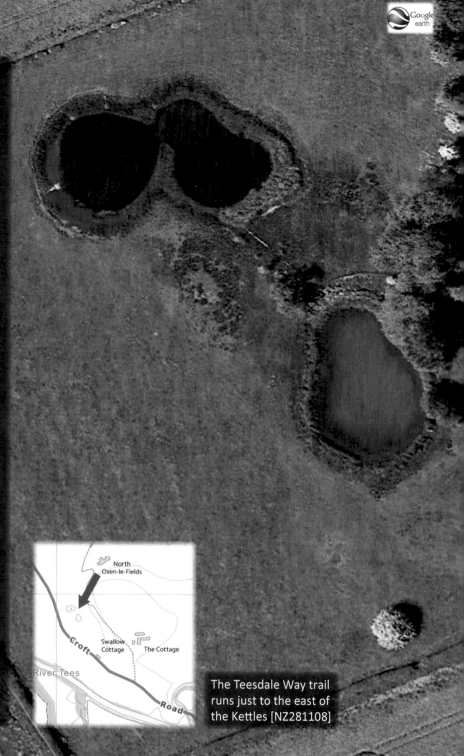

# Hell Kettles

**In a narrow ribbon of land between Darlington and Doncaster is a rock that dissolves in water more quickly than most others in Britain: gypsum. Hell Kettles is just one of many places where this is happening.**

Gypsum is hydrated calcium sulphate ($CaSO_4.2H_2O$) and is a type of rock called an evaporite. It occurs as layers in rocks that were once muds and salts on the shallow margins of a warm sea. The sea was constantly evaporating and leaving thick deposits of gypsum, salt, limestones and mudstones. That was 250 million years ago on the borderline between the Permian and Triassic periods. The land we now call Britain was about 25 degrees north of the Equator then, the same latitude as Dubai today. The deposits of that warm sea are the reason behind the water-filled holes known as Hell Kettles. The holes were caused by the gypsum layers underground dissolving in water flowing through the fissures and joints in the rocks. The rock layers above then break up and collapse and ultimately the ground surface subsides. The greater the subterranean water flow the faster the gypsum dissolves. A block the size of a transit van can disappear in around five years!  That's why these areas not good places to site anything that may increase water flow, such as quarries and mines, or boreholes for irrigation or ground-source heat-pumps. At Hell Kettles and nearby, the groundwater is flowing naturally to the surface and it is warm enough to steam and not freeze in winter!

As the name suggests there's a lot of folklore about Hell Kettles (the first recorded collapse was in 1179). They are supposedly bottomless (in reality around seven metres deep) and saw the demise of blaspheming farmers, Henry VIII's ducks and an Asian diver. While this is all myth there is another fabulous tale, one with some science behind it. A British expert on gypsum geology suggested that Alice's fall into Wonderland owed its origin to Lewis Carroll (aka Charles Dodgson), once living close to Hell Kettles. More, the girl who was the model for the illustrations of Alice, Mary Badcock, lived near a gypsum collapse hole at Ripon, where Carroll's father was a canon at the Cathedral. QED! Ripon is 50 kilometres further south, but in the same gypsum rock ribbon. The problem of gypsum subsidence in the city is so severe that it has resulted in the collapse of buildings and the abandonment of several more. Dissolving rock is more than a literary or geological curiosity.

The Teesdale Way trail runs just to the east of the Kettles [NZ281108]

The southern Kettle. It is a blue-green colour and is fed directly by groundwater

# Hown's Gill

You see sandstone everywhere in Durham, in the natural landscape of the west and north and in buildings across the whole county. Stone farmhouses and walls, castles and a cathedral are at the core of the region's character and image.

The quarry on the side of Hown's Gill near Consett is just one of hundreds if not thousands of abandoned sandstone quarries in the region. Once sand in a large river flowing through tropical swamps around 315 million years ago, it is now rock, and a part of the youngest bit of Carboniferous called the Westphalian (better known in Britain as the Coal Measures). This 25-metre-thick sandstone lies between the Marshall Green and Victoria coal seams that used to be mined across the whole of northeast England. Hown's Quarry was one of the larger workings in the region and it was unusual in that the stone was also quarried underground. Those galleries still exist today but they are dangerous. While sandstone is never likely to be quarried on the same scale as in the past, it will still be needed, not only so that new buildings fit well with local architecture but for the continuing repairs to buildings that are important to our heritage.

Walk down Hown's Gill today and you might see climbers on the rock face, many of them doing more than 40 'sport' routes. Don't miss Hownsgill viaduct, opened in 1858 to replace Robert Stephenson's rope-worked inclines on the limestone-carrying Stanhope to Consett rail line. The bridge, built to cross a valley cut by glacial meltwater as the Ice Age ended, is over 200 metres long and 45 metres high and made of three million white firebricks. It's nice to see that the architect used sandstone here and there though.

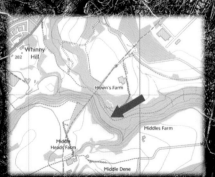

There is a car park north of Hown's Farm. It is less than 1 kilometre to the quarry. You can see it from the footpath, please do not enter the galleries [NZ097489]

Galleries in Hown's sandstone quarry

# Little Scar and Long Scar

These two small outcrops in the bay at Seaton Carew are the only place in Durham where rocks from the Triassic period of Earth's history are seen at the surface.

These are the youngest sedimentary rocks in this book. They tell of a time, around 245 million years ago, when Durham was a continental desert about 30 degrees north of the Equator. There are about 20 square kilometres of them in the southeast of the county but except for Little and Long Scars they are hidden, covered by thick layers of clay, sand and mud left since the last ice sheet melted 15,000 years ago.

The rocks at Little and Long Scars are mostly red sandstones but there are some mudstones and siltstones too. Some of the rocks of Little Scar slope steeply to the north but there are other layers at different angles (called cross-bedding), these and the fossil ripple marks and possible desiccation cracks, point to them being deposited on land but in shallow and temporary water bodies.

Less than four metres thickness of these rocks is visible on the foreshore but 10 kilometres inland one borehole proved more than 200 metres. Geologists used to call rocks of this age New Red Sandstone but then adopted the name Bunter Sandstone from Germany as this was where they could best be seen. Their name changed again and they are now known as the Sherwood Sandstone – the very same rocks that you will see in the ancient caves under Nottingham Castle and in the high cliffs on the west coast at St Bees Head in Cumbria.

Digital scans of County Series geological maps surveyed around 1876 © UKRI 2023. Derived from British Geological Survey Map Portal under the Open Government Licence.

Little Scar is just beside the promenade at Seaton Carew [NZ525304]

Red Triassic sandstone forming Little Scar rocks

# Middridge Quarry

**Running north to south through Durham and all the way to Nottinghamshire is a rock that tells a tale of a dramatic rise in sea level around 260 million years ago. It is called the Marl Slate but it is neither a marl nor a slate.**

The desert and its yellow sand dunes that began the Permian period were rapidly inundated by an ancient sea, the Zechstein, which extended from eastern England to Poland. The Marl Slate was the first rock deposited in that sea. It is made of thin layers of limestone and siltstone and smells of oil when it is freshly broken. Its composition and the fossils in it have puzzled geologists but the current theory is that it formed in relatively shallow and sometimes stagnant lagoons behind coastal barriers. Middridge Quarry is one of few places where you can see the Marl Slate, the desert dunes below and the limestones above. Most of the other localities where the rock is exposed (quarries, rail and road cuttings) are no longer visible or accessible.

The Marl Slate is famous for its fossil fish but also for reptiles and plants which grew at the margins of the sea. One of those fish is called 'Palaeoniscus'. It had hard scales and sharp teeth and grew to around 30 centimetres. It was a predator and hunted other small fish and animals. Palaeoniscus became extinct but its relatives are all the 30,000 ray-finned fish species alive today. The old quarry at Middridge has produced not only fish but some of the best-preserved plant fossils in England and early reptile bones too. For these reasons it is protected as a Site of Special Scientific Interest (SSSI). As this book was being prepared and as perverse as it sounds given the incredible story the quarry's fossils have to tell, an application to use it for landfill had been submitted to the Council. There was much opposition and happily the decision was 'refuse'.

From Middridge village take the footpath south for about 1 kilometre [NZ248252]

Fossil of the Permian fish Palaeoniscus from the Marl Slate [P552051]. © UKRI. All rights reserved (British Geological Survey permit number CP23/005)

# North Grain

**In the side of a small stream called North Grain, below a bend in the Rookhope – Allenheads road, is a cliff made of shale.**

Shale, mudstone and siltstone are all terms used for fine-grained sedimentary rocks. They are usually dark grey, thinly layered (laminated) and relatively soft and you will hear geologists describe them as being fissile. Shales make up a lot of the Carboniferous rocks in Durham, but unless you look carefully in river banks or old quarries you seldom see them. They don't create prominent features in the landscape like harder sandstones and limestones. For that reason (and unlike those harder rocks) it is rare that they have been given specific names by geologists, miners and quarrymen. The rocks at North Grain are typical anonymous Carboniferous shales. Shales were originally mud and fine organic debris and with sand, were brought down by rivers onto floodplains, into coastal lagoons and the sea. Sea level and river flows fluctuated many times in the Carboniferous and so the sediments changed too, from muds to silts and sands and back again.

The shale cliff is cut by a near-vertical fault and bright orange-coloured, iron-rich water flows out of it. This is typical too; shales contain a lot of iron which can oxidize and result in springs and streams that are heavily discoloured. Discharges rich in iron may cause problems for small off-grid domestic water supplies and are also commonly associated with water that flows from old coal mine workings, where they can be a much more serious issue, because of iron's effect on water treatment, as well as taste and staining.

There is a small pull-in on the east bound side of the road. It's about 100 metres south to the cliff [NY882449]

Shale exposed in cliff above North Grain stream. Iron-rich water runs from a small fault cutting the shales

# Pallis Burn

In the tributaries that flow into the River Derwent between Chopwell and Winlaton are very recent geological deposits that are uncommon in Britain. Some of these fragile deposits, called tufa, occur in Pallis Burn, near Victoria Garesfield.

Tufa is a very modern limestone, essentially calcium carbonate - it's sometimes called travertine. Here it forms small moss-covered dams (barrages) across the streams and often incorporates twigs and leaves and even discarded plastic. Tufa usually occurs where much older limestones are nearby; for example, the famous Dropping Well of Mother Shipton's Cave in Yorkshire. Rain or groundwater dissolves the calcium carbonate and then re-deposits it. But in this part of Durham, the nearby rocks are not limestones, they are mostly Carboniferous sandstones, shales and coals, so why is the tufa forming? One theory is that it is formed by an upwelling of warmer water from much deeper rocks heated by the underlying Weardale granite. Another is that it forms through the action of bacteria and other microbes on organic debris. Or maybe it's a bit of both.

Many tufa barrages are less than a few hundred years old. They are very delicate and at risk from changes in water chemistry, brought on by deforestation and human pollution. They are also susceptible to physical damage. These tufa deposits are mentioned as one of several sites of Local Geological Interest. If you visit please take only photographs.

Chopwell Woods has a large car park. Walk southeast along the track and to reach the burn scramble into the valley [NZ144577]

Tufa barrages in Pallis Burn

# Roker

The Magnesian Limestone is perhaps the most famous of Durham's rocks. It tells a story of barrier reefs and a warm sea that kept evaporating in the hot sun when our part of the world was just like Australia's west coast.

Roker is just one of many places along the Durham coast where you can see rocks that were once limy mud and animals living on and beside a reef in a tropical sea just 10 degrees north of the Equator. The story began around 260 million years ago in the Permian period when a northern ocean burst into a low basin between what are now Britain and Poland. It created a sea called the Zechstein which was less than 300 metres deep and along its western coast, where Durham is now, there were barrier reefs. In the water, either side of the reefs, different types of limestone were deposited (magnesium carbonate: dolomite, as well as calcium carbonate). As the sea water kept evaporating salts like anhydrite and halite were deposited too. Fluctuating sea levels and instability in the reef zone meant huge areas of semi-solidified limestones slumped and slid down the slopes. In the millions of years that followed some of the limestones were recrystallized into weird shapes, like the 'cannonballs' you see at Roker.

Despite the harsh salty environment, animals thrived here and built up the reefs. There are many fossils in the Magnesian Limestone: shellfish, algae, plankton and primitive animals called bryozoa that lived in colonies and looked like twigs or fans. Like many rocks which are special and famous, the Magnesian Limestone has been studied intensively by geologists over more than 150 years. Our understanding of how it formed and the sequence of events has developed; some of the names of the rocks changed with that improved interpretation. So, if you hear terms like Raisby, Ford and Roker formations, don't worry, just think Magnesian Limestone!

On the foreshore just below the promenade [NZ407595]

The cannonball limestone on the foreshore at Roker

# Tunstall Hills

**These two hills, a rocky one and a green one, give a great view over Sunderland and the country to the south. Walk up them and you will be standing on a 255-million-year-old barrier reef.**

Today that reef stretches north-south as a ridge more than 30 kilometres long. Back in the Permian period, open sea was to your east and a large shallow salty bay was to your west. The climate was hot and arid then and the water in the bay kept evaporating producing thick layers of salts. The reef is mostly made of up of a limy mud, the debris from shells, algae and bryozoa that lived on and around the reef. These limestones in eastern Durham are traditionally called Magnesian Limestones because they have variable amounts of magnesium carbonate in them. The pages on Roker and Marsden will give you more information on the way these limestones were formed.... and then deformed.

Pale yellow and grey Magnesian Limestone is something you see often while travelling through Durham on the A1 or East Coast main line. It appears in road and rail cuttings and hillsides and in many working and abandoned quarries. Today the limestones are mostly used in construction, for fill and hardcore, but they have also been used as a building stone, as a flux in steel making, for refractory bricks and as a source of magnesium for the pharmaceutical and electrical insulation industries.

Rocks are a big influence on plants and wildlife; scientists talk about geodiversity as a foundation of biodiversity. Tunstall Hills are a great example of this. Magnesian Limestone produces thin soils rich in lime and these have characteristic plants like common rockrose, birds-foot trefoil and blue moor grass. This habitat, both the plants and rocks beneath, are rare (they are designated as Sites of Special Scientific Interest: SSSIs) and initiatives such as the Limestone Landscapes project were set up to conserve and protect them.

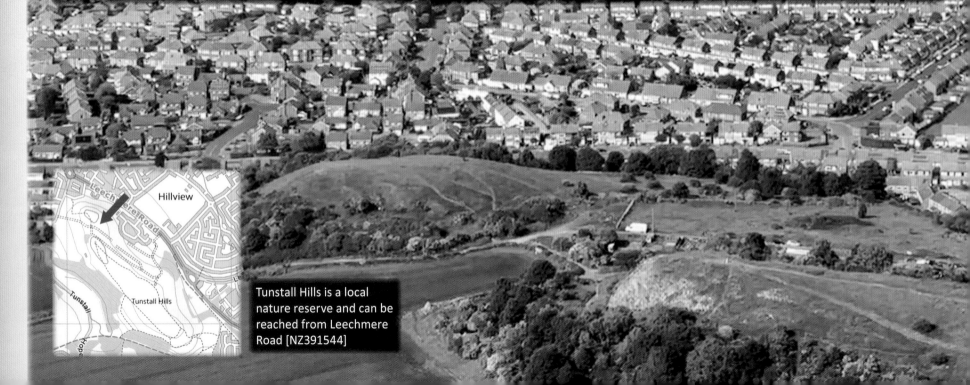

Tunstall Hills is a local nature reserve and can be reached from Leechmere Road [NZ391544]

Tunstall Hills: the southern 'Rocky' hill from the northern 'Green' hill

# Cockfield Fell

**Trying to work out the geology of the landscape is sometimes not so much about where rocks are, as where they once were. Cockfield Fell is just like that.**

Take the road past the cemetery to the northeast of the village and you will come across a long trench heading east. It used to head west too but it has been landfilled. This is an old quarry where they dug out a hard igneous rock called dolerite. It is a section of the Cleveland – Armathwaite Dyke and at 60 million years old it is the youngest bit of solid rock in this book. Back then northwestern Britain was feeling the effects of the beginning of the opening of the Atlantic Ocean. Vast amounts of lava was erupting from vents in Scotland and Northern Ireland, and as the Earth's crust was being stretched, cracks opened up and within them thin near-vertical blades of molten rock radiated out across the country. This dyke, thought to be part of a 'swarm' from the Isle of Mull, is one of these blades.

The dyke varies in thickness but even at its usual maximum, around 30 metres, it is not very wide given how many kilometres long it is. How far it travelled laterally from Mull, or whether it pulsed up from below is still debated. This probably wasn't a question that troubled quarrymen; they had been tracing the dyke cross country for at least 250 years. You can find their diggings in it for roadstone further east at Bolam too.

The preservation of the Fell at Cockfield is unusual for a place that is 'lowland'. But visit and you will see that that conservation means there are not only the scars of dolerite quarrying but the humps and bumps of coal mining and settlement since medieval times too. With all this history in one place you won't be surprised to hear that the Fell is a Scheduled Ancient Monument.

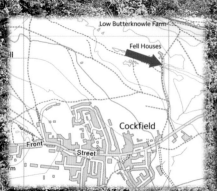

Walk from the village along the road past the cemetery onto the Fell [NZ130248]

Cockfield Fell. Position of photo shown by blue arrow.
Digital surface model at >1 metre vertical accuracy:
Environment Agency data processed by GIS software

# High Force

High Force is stunning! It is no surprise that it is one of the most iconic and visited locations in Durham. 'Force' comes from foss, a Viking name for waterfall.

The River Tees drops 21 metres over the hard dolerite of the Whin Sill, a once molten rock that was injected between older Carboniferous strata 295 million years ago. You can see the characteristic vertical columns and joints in the dolerite caused by it cooling and shrinking. Look beneath the Whin Sill and you will see darker sandstone and limestone layers. These 330-million-year-old softer sedimentary rocks are slowly but steadily being eroded back by the river until eventually the overlying dolerite is undercut and collapses. All waterfalls move slowly upstream as nature re-profiles the river bed. 2.5 kilometres downstream is Low Force, a smaller but no less beautiful waterfall also flowing over the Whin Sill. If you walk just downstream of Wynch Bridge on the south bank, beneath a large knoll of Whin Sill there is a huge tilted 'raft' (block) of sandstone and siltstone, 2 metres thick and over 70 metres long. It once formed the roof of the chamber of molten dolerite rock and then fell into it and was changed (metamorphosed) into a rock geologists call a hornfels and quarrymen and miners called whetstone.

The River Tees at Low Force was used as a location in the recent war film 1917. There's no Whin Sill in northern France and Teesdale is a long way from the soft Cretaceous rocks of Salisbury Plain where much of the rest of the movie was shot. But, to the irritation of many geologists, film directors are not too troubled by rock continuity. Watch the rapid transit of Robin Hood, Prince of Thieves from the white cliffs of Sussex to Sycamore Gap, or Uhtred's escape from the 'Icelandic' beach in The Last Kingdom; in reality Blast Beach south of Seaham. It's ok, I know.... us rock folk suffer from imagination deficit disorder.

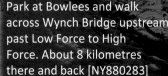

Park at Bowlees and walk across Wynch Bridge upstream past Low Force to High Force. About 8 kilometres there and back [NY880283]

High Force

# Holwick Scars

**These dramatic, north facing cliffs with their rolling top are one of many places in Teesdale where the Whin Sill stands out in the landscape.**

It stands out because the rock is hard and resists erosion. You can see that durability well here, in the cliffs at Cronkley Fell and the waterfalls of High and Low Force and Cauldron Snout. Quarrymen named the Whin Sill. Whin because it is so hard and, when you hit it, that's the sound it makes, and sill because it's horizontal. For geologists the Whin Sill is special – this is the original sill in Earth Science and gave the name 'sill' to all other similar rock formations worldwide. The Whin Sill is made of a rock called dolerite. It was injected horizontally between older (Carboniferous) rock layers as molten magma around 295 million years ago. At 1100°C it was hot enough to change the character of the rocks immediately above and below it; some limestones became marble. As the magma cooled it contracted, producing the typical vertical fractures and columns – not quite as perfect as those hexagonal columns of the Giant's Causeway or Staffa, but the same process.

The Scars owe their current shape not just to the relative hardness of the rock, but also to a geological fault, plus millions of years of erosion. Only 20,000 years ago glaciers and their meltwater were scouring out the valley of the Tees, and as the scree slopes at the foot of the Scars show, weathering of the cliffs continues today. When the ice finally melted away around 12,000 years ago Teesdale was again colonized by plants and trees. Some of those early plants continue to grow here today making Teesdale a renowned botanical hotspot. Around 8000 years ago our ancestors returned to live here too and the land below the cliffs has many signs of human occupation.

Park at Bowlees. It is a 2 kilometre walk across the Tees at Wynch Bridge and south to the Scars [NY902269]

Holwick Scars

# Rookhope

From Rookhope village go southwest across the bridge and turn southeast along the path beside the burn [NY937427]

**High up in Weardale is a small village, Rookhope. It is known to geologists all over the world because here in 1960 they drilled a borehole deep into the Earth to see whether theories about what might be found below the Pennine hills were right.**

In 1933 a young geologist was studying the distribution of minerals in the north Pennines. He came to the conclusion that because the minerals occur in concentric zones, a large granite body deep down was responsible, one which never appears at the surface. Around 20 years later another Durham University scientist measured subtle variations in the gravity of the Earth here and recognised that in this part of the Pennines the Earth's crust is anomalously light. He arrived at the same conclusion, so a borehole was drilled, hitting granite at 390 metres below the surface. The rock became known as the Weardale Granite and it is made of interlocking crystals of quartz, feldspar and mica. When it was dated it was around 410 million years old. That made it a lot older than the mineral veins around it and so it couldn't have been responsible for the minerals! Research - and the debate - continues.

The temperature at the final depth of the borehole (about 800 metres) was around 40°C. To see if there was potential for geothermal energy another hole was drilled more recently at Eastgate. That proved the granite's existence 272 metres down. It is now believed to be part of a larger body of rock; a 'batholith' that stretches from Rowlands Gill to Dufton in Cumbria. Because of its size and 'crustal buoyancy' geologists think it had a profound influence on the way all the Carboniferous rocks across the north of England were deposited.

While new data and techniques may have overturned earlier theories, that early research changed forever the way Earth scientists the world over think about granites and minerals. Not surprisingly both scientists went on to have stellar careers. The young geologist, Sir Kingsley Dunham, received 12 honorary doctorates and became Director of the British Geological Survey while Martin Bott became an eminent professor at Durham University and trained generations of geophysicists.

You can still visit the borehole site today. While care was taken at the time to securely cap it, local youths dropped iron bars down it so this window deep into the Earth can no longer be used for research. Happily, the core samples that were taken from the borehole were conserved and can still be studied.

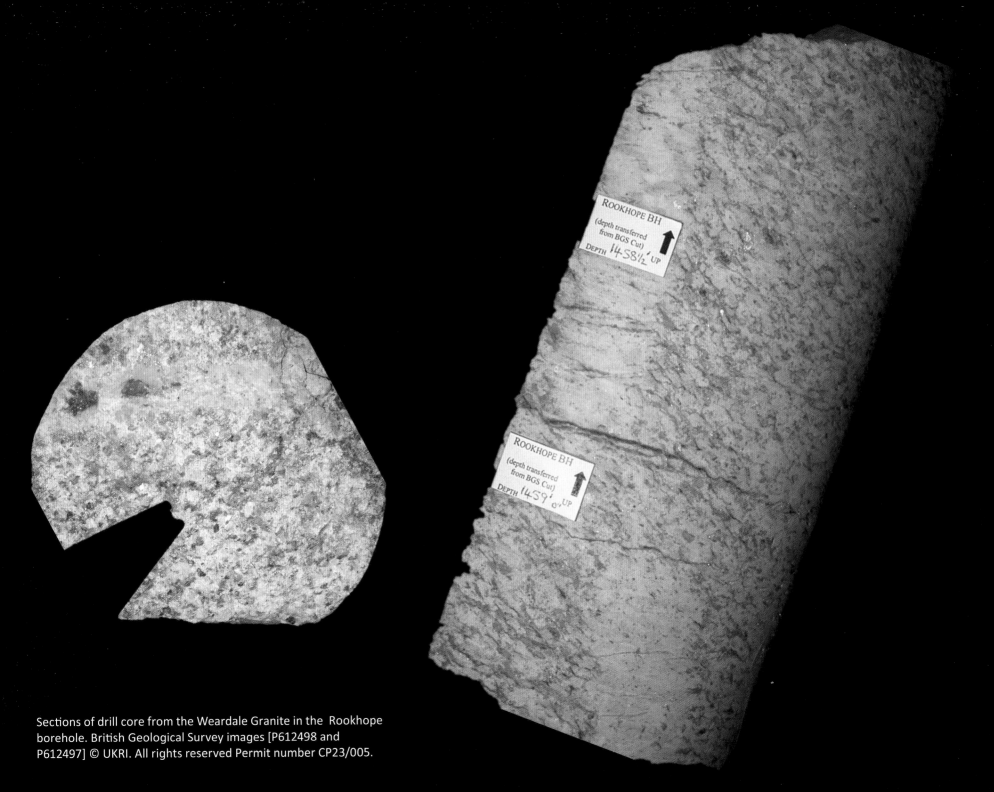

Sections of drill core from the Weardale Granite in the Rookhope borehole. British Geological Survey images [P612498 and P612497] © UKRI. All rights reserved Permit number CP23/005.

ROOKHOPE BH
(depth transferred from BGS Cut)
DEPTH 1458½' UP

ROOKHOPE BH
(depth transferred from BGS Cut)
DEPTH 1459' 0" UP

# Stanhope

**There are a few rocky reasons to include the town of Stanhope in this book. It is here in the molten rock section because of the Whin Sill. Not the Great Whin Sill, but the Little Whin Sill.**

Yes, there is more than one Sill. Up and downstream of old Stanhope Bridge the River Wear runs in a ruler-straight, narrow channel eroded through the Little Whin Sill. Like its big brother this Sill is the same very hard rock called dolerite; a bit of the same molten magma that was also injected horizontally between Carboniferous sedimentary rocks around 295 million years ago at the very beginning of the Permian period. When geologists first started to study the Whin Sill (northern quarrymen's terms for a hard, level rock) they debated whether it was lava that had flowed on the surface or a molten rock intruded underground. They concluded it was an intrusion: a single layer of rock that stayed at a consistent horizontal level. Embarrassingly, many years later it became apparent that the Whin Sill did not conform to its own definition. It transgressed, literally - it moved between different layers of strata. Worse, it seemed that there was more than one Whin Sill. So today you will hear geologists talk of the Whin Sill suite, or complex. The Little Whin Sill is part of that. But with a collective area of at least 4500 square kilometres, most of it beneath the surface, these well-connected bits of rock are England's most extensive igneous intrusion.

Stanhope has other geological claims to fame. There is the vast Ashes limestone quarry and its waste heaps overlooking the town. More famously, there is a fossil tree stump built into the wall of the churchyard. The stump was discovered with others in 1915 in a sandstone quarry at nearby Edmundbyers Cross. This tree was growing in a tropical swamp 320 million years ago when Britain was just a few degrees from the Equator. After the tree died and rotted river sand replaced the trunk and roots and left them as a cast in the sandstone. The name of the plant is Sigillaria, a forerunner of today's small club mosses. Back then they grew to a staggering 30 metres tall!

From Stanhope cross the stepping stones and walk the riverside footpath or drive west until you reach Stanhope Bridge [NY985390]

River Wear cutting through Little Whin Sill at Stanhope Bridge

# Widdybank Fell

If you walk from the car park at Cow Green reservoir to Cauldron Snout waterfall you cross the western edge of Widdybank Fell. The fell is one of the top five botanical hotspots in Britain. It's no coincidence that one of its rocks is special too.

Locally called the Sugar Limestone, it started as a pure limestone of Carboniferous age then was baked by the intrusion of Whin Sill dolerite beneath it. The 1100°C molten magma 'cooked' the limestone into a crumbly 'sugary' marble. Now natural weathering is reducing the marble to something that looks like white coarse sand. The process of changing rocks by heat and/or pressure is called metamorphism and this is one of only a few places in the county where you can see a metamorphic rock.

Look out for 'flushes' where water flows out between the base of the limestone and the top of the impervious Whin Sill. These and other local habitats support a variety of rare plants such as spring gentian, yellow saxifrage, alpine rush, bird's-eye primrose, dwarf milkwort, Teesdale violet, spring-sedge and hoary rock-rose. These are plants that endure in the harsh climate of the Pennine uplands and may have survived for perhaps 12,000 years since vegetation re-colonized the fells after the last Ice Age. These plants are vulnerable, so please keep to the marked footpath.

From the car park at Cow Green reservoir head south along the footpath towards the dam [NZ817296]

Tormentil and dwarf milkwort

The 'Sugar Limestone'

# Burtreeford

Tilted rocks in the River Wear at Burteeford

The Burtreeford Disturbance might sound like a rowdy night in a Weardale pub that got out of hand but it's not. It's a very big bit of geological disruption in the north Pennines.

The Disturbance is a combination of folding, faulting and general dislocation of the rocks stretching around 40 kilometres from Lunedale in the south, to Allenheads in Northumberland in the north. Theoretical modelling of the hidden Weardale granite and rocks around it shows scientists the Disturbance goes deep. It is a major feature of the geological structure of northern England, perhaps penetrating thousands of metres into the Earth's crust. Despite its size and significance, it's a shy and retiring feature at the surface with little evidence of its presence or magnitude which explains why it is not well understood.

When did the Burtreeford Disturbance take place? Recent research has looked at structures in the north Pennines including large and small faults and dated the rocks by measuring the decay of radioactive elements. It concluded this huge zone of bending and breaking is around 300 million years old. This is about the same age as the intrusion of the Whin Sill. The Durham University scientists who did the research think the Burtreeford Disturbance may have been a major conduit for hot mineral-rich fluids which formed the north Pennine ore fields and that this is all linked with the injection of the Whin Sill. These connections upset the geological applecart because they challenged decades of thinking about the way that mineral deposits here and elsewhere in the world were formed.

Less than 500 metres from Burtreeford you can see all of the rocks that are part of this radical geological interpretation. In the River Wear upstream of Cowshill the Carboniferous limestones and sandstones are tilted by as much as 50° from horizontal. Whin Sill dolerite is revealed in the old Copthill quarry while extensive spoil heaps in the valley of Sedling Burn provide graphic evidence of the minerals and their exploitation.

Take footpaths along the River Wear to see the dipping rocks and Copthill Whin Sill and up Sedling Burn to see the mineral workings [NY856406]

Old ironstone workings and waste in the valley of Sedling Burn

# Butterknowle

**Butterknowle is a small village with a deep secret. It has a seriously big fracture in the Earth's crust underneath it.**

Geological faults are a bit like cracks in your house walls. Sometimes they are shallow and restricted to the near-surface rocks; equivalent to the plaster. Sometimes they go all the way through the bricks and no matter how many times you fill the plaster the cracks keep coming back. That's what this extremely big crack, the Butterknowle Fault, does; it's deep and it has kept moving.

The Fault (more a zone of faults at the surface) runs west to east across Durham from Eggleston to Hartlepool and forms the southern limit of a major geological chunk of the north Pennines called the 'Alston Block'. It is probably related to the collision of two ancient continents and started moving at least 400 million years ago. Geophysical surveys and modelling show it dislocating deep, older rocks that we rarely see by almost 5 kilometres beneath Butterknowle! Several thousand metres of Carboniferous and Permian strata were deposited unevenly on top of them, and because the fault had acted like a hinge, the rocks are thicker to the south than the north. Fast forward a 100 million years or so and the Fault moved yet again (geologists would say 'reactivated'), but this time not quite as much, around 200 metres vertically. That was quite enough to upset 19th century Durham miners who found their coal seams disappeared, only to appear again at a very different level on the other side of the Fault.

Geologists still get excited about the Fault and its deep structure and origin is a topic of lively debate. Despite the fact that the Butterknowle Fault is huge it's not obvious in the rocks at the surface and the deposits of the last Ice Age have not helped by papering over this crack in the geological bricks and plaster. Drive through the village and you'd never know what lies beneath.

**BUTTERKNOWLE**
*Please drive carefully*
*Seriously big fault*

Butterknowle village is 6 kilometres west of West Auckland [NZ106257]

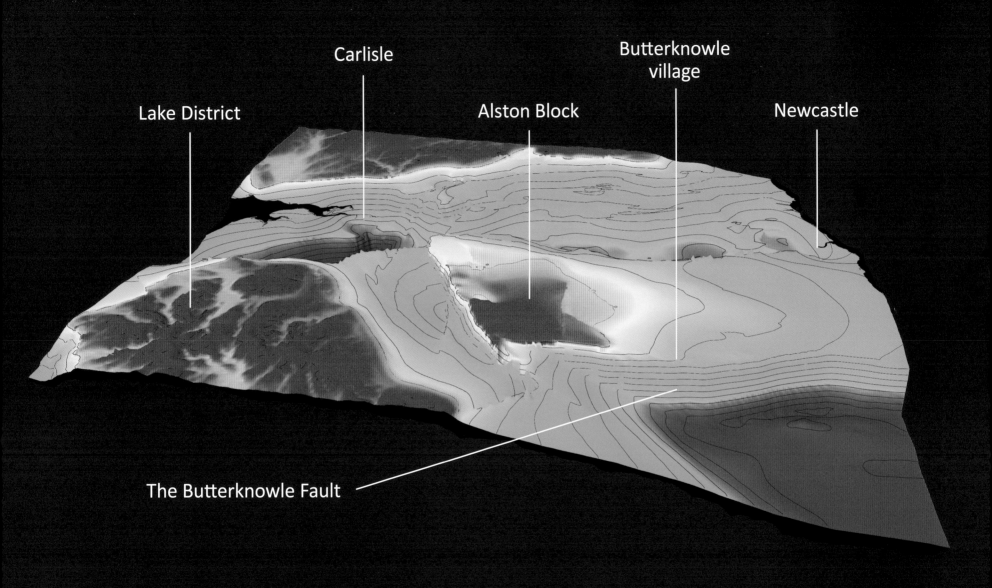

Lake District

Carlisle

Butterknowle village

Alston Block

Newcastle

The Butterknowle Fault

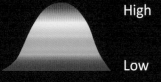

High

Low

A model of the surface of the older rocks based on geophysical data. The older rocks are exposed in the Lake District but buried deep beneath Carboniferous and younger rocks elsewhere. Red is higher, blue is lower and the contours are at 500 metre intervals. Source digital data provided by British Geological Survey (Licence 2023/059) © UKRI. All rights reserved

# 22

# Houghton-le-Spring

Two sets of rocks are the stars of this tale. South and west of the town are coals, sandstones and shales of the Carboniferous and sitting on top of them to the north are younger Permian limestones and sandstones.

Houghton-le-Spring colliery operated from 1823 to 1981 and was one of the first to exploit the coals concealed beneath the Permian rocks. It shared many things with other northeastern collieries, but two are relevant to this story. Houghton miners encountered faults, near-vertical breaks in the rock that could run for kilometres, dislocating the seams. They also had to keep the pit dry by pumping water out; when the coalfield stopped working many mine pumps were switched off and water levels started to rise. Drive through the A690 Houghton Cut and you get a roadside view of the younger, overlying Permian rocks: now dirty but once pale cream dolomitic (Magnesian) limestones. You will notice lots of fissures and cracks often caused by the rock layers below dissolving and collapsing naturally. Wire netting has been erected to stop rock falls. Around 2001 a line of cracks opened up across the road and fissures appeared in fields on either side. Geologists surveyed the area using detailed geological maps, coal mine plans and even geophysics to assess the voids underground. They discovered that directly beneath this line of cracks was a fault, one that cut through the coal seams below. If the fault was to blame, why did the cracks open up now when mining had finished 20 years before? Their conclusion was that water levels in the mine had risen after the pumps were switched off, causing subsidence, re-activating the fault and disturbing the weak limestone above.

There are several places in Durham where there are similar rocks, fault lines and water-filled mine workings. The problems they cause are not restricted to cracking roads. Fissures beneath landfill sites located in old quarries in Permian rocks are a concern as they could contaminate groundwater in the Yellow Sands aquifer between the coal mines and the limestone. Mine water is also contaminated with minerals from coal seams. Predicting how that water moves is notoriously difficult and the threat of it entering the region's water supplies is something that is constantly monitored.

A690 road through the Houghton Cut [NZ343504]

Magnesian Limestone in the A690 Houghton Cut

# Marsden Bay

# 23

**The cliffs here are one of the best places in Britain to see what happens when thick layers of soluble rocks underground dissolve and the strata above them collapse.**

The cliffs are made of the Concretionary Limestone Formation, a section of the Magnesian Limestone. That's from the Permian period around 255 million years ago. It was once limy mud and the fragmented remains of sea creatures on the slopes of a shallow sea. In limestone blocks on the modern foreshore, you might see the moulds of fossil seashells very much like clams. Beneath this limestone there used to be layers of 'evaporites' like anhydrite, gypsum and rock salt (aka table salt) that formed as the shallow sea slowly disappeared because of arid conditions. Evaporites like these can easily dissolve and in the millions of years that followed groundwater moving through slowly widened cracks and fissures and completely removed them. That caused the limestone above to drop down around 80 metres. Some parts seem to have subsided gently but the broken and messed up rocks elsewhere in the cliff face show how the collapse must sometimes have been catastrophic. Look carefully at the limestone and you'll see evidence of older folding and faulting caused by the slumping and sliding before the rocks were completely solidified. The pages about Roker and Tunstall have other information about the Magnesian Limestone. Please do not get too close to the cliff face, it is unstable as the collapse of the arch of Marsden Rock in 1996 and many other sea stacks along the Durham coast shows.

Take the steps to the beach beside Marsden Grotto pub. Be aware of tide times. [NZ400649]

Collapsed and folded strata in the Magnesian Limestone

# 24

# Middlehope Burn

**Middlehope Burn above Westgate is crossed by a geological fault, an east-west fracture in the bedrock that dislocates one side relative to the other. In common with many other faults in this part of the Pennines this one is occupied by a mineral vein.**

There were major mine workings associated with the vein in Middlehope Burn, and because they are typical of north Pennine mining practices and the remains are relatively well preserved, they are a Scheduled Ancient Monument. The vein within the fault is known as the Slit (or Slitt) Vein. You can tell you are approaching the fault by the way the layers of sandstone start to slope at greater angles in the stream. Miners in the past knew mineral-rich veins were often associated with faults and used rocks at strange angles to locate them. As well as mining along the length of the vein at surface they sunk a shaft and passages 178 metres deep; some of the deepest in Weardale.

500 metres east beside the Westgate to Rookhope road is West Rigg Opencut, an iron ore opencast working which clearly shows the line of the vein and fault left behind as a prominent unquarried rib. The Slit vein is composed of several minerals including galena (lead), siderite (iron), fluorite, and quartz. Little of the waste material from processing the ore is visible at the mine beside the burn now, but if you hike a further 800 metres upstream you will come across mine dumps that do contain these minerals.

As well as its geological and industrial archaeological significance Middlehope Burn mine site has a botanical interest. Some of the plants that grow here, like spring sandwort and mountain pansy, are able to tolerate soils contaminated with heavy metals and these 'calaminarian' plants and the woodland ecology of the valley mean this is a Site of Special Scientific Interest (SSSI).

Walk north for about a kilometre along the Burn from Westgate [NY906391]

West Rigg Opencut: an iron ore quarry which exposed the vertical void left after lead mining in the Slit Vein

# Salterfen Point

# 25

Geologists obviously spend a lot of time on the rocks and fossils we can see and sample. You might think we spend a lot less time studying the millions of years of rocks that have been eroded away and are no longer there. But those gaps are important.

Stand on the clifftop at Ryhope and look towards Salterfen Point. The bottom part of the cliffs is pale-yellow Permian limestones around 255 million years old. Above and slumping over them is soft stony brown clay, silt and sand, deposited by ice sheets less than 20,000 years ago. The dividing line is called an 'unconformity' and it represents a gap of 255 million years in the geological history of Durham. That doesn't mean that no other rocks were deposited in that long period, they were. It's just that whatever Triassic, Jurassic and Cretaceous rocks were there, probably thousands of metres of them, have all been eroded away. To see those younger rocks you're going to have to travel south into Yorkshire. The unconformity at Salterfen Point is not unique. There is a 50-million-year gap between Durham's Carboniferous and Permian rocks too. That gap represents a time when mountains were being built and then eroded into a rocky desert. You can see this unconformity at Castletown beside the River Wear in Sunderland where the older sandstone is reddened because it was once the desert floor. At Cronkley in Upper Teesdale, 485-million-year-old Ordovician slates and lavas lie beneath the 350-million-year-old Carboniferous rocks; any intervening Silurian and Devonian rocks are gone.

It was an unconformity at another northeast coast location, Siccar Point in Berwickshire, that provided rational evidence that the church's once literal view of 'Creation' was wrong. The world did not begin on Sunday 23 October 4004 BC, as Archbishop Ussher, a 17th century Primate of all Ireland had calculated, but was many millions of years old. That discovery, made by geologist James Hutton in 1788, challenged the widely held interpretation of the scriptures, and led to accusations of blasphemy and atheism. Hutton compounded these sins when he came to another conclusion about our planet "We find no vestige of a beginning, no prospect of an end." Who said rocks don't have anything profound to say?

Salterfen Rocks

Walk along the England Coast Path. You can access it from Ryhope [NZ414539]

Glacial clay, silt, sand and stones
lying on Magnesian Limestone

# 26

# Burnhope Seat

**Almost 20% of Durham is upland moor and much of that is blanket bog. This is a very rare landscape in Britain and in Europe. Durham for its size probably has the largest share: tens of thousands of hectares of it.**

Peat (bog or mire) is regarded as a legitimate bit of geology, as you will see by its inclusion on British Geological Survey maps. Burnhope Seat seemed an appropriate place to choose for this book, not least because of its claim to be, at 747 metres, the highest point in Durham and also because by the time you've squelched to its summit on the county border you will have become very familiar with the endearing qualities of upland peat. Vast swathes of living and decaying heather, sphagnum moss, cotton grass and many other plants that hold and hide a lot of water make for tough going. Beneath the living surface layer can be more than two metres of dark brown peat, often exposed in the hags you will negotiate. These upland moors are home to some rare wildlife and while you may not be lucky enough to spot a hen harrier hunting, you could see and hear flocks of golden plovers.

Peat bogs are more than special habitats. They store twice as much carbon per hectare as forests, and if they are drained, that $CO_2$ contributes to global warming. They hold back water preventing flooding in the valleys below and they provide a reservoir for clean water supplies. But it is an upland environment that is under threat from incoming unwelcome plants, burning and draining by us and damage by natural and over-grazing erosion - the many gullies and hags in the moor testify to that. Awareness of the importance of peat at last seems to be registering with us and our politicians. Go hike across Burnhope Seat or any of the Durham moors and you will experience a landscape that is rare in England, one that on a cold day can look and feel more like high Arctic tundra than modest Pennine hills. 8000 years ago, as plants and trees steadily re-occupied the hills and valleys, Stone Age people hunted here at the margins of the forest and the moor. Visit: you'll have the place to yourself and it won't be hard to imagine that.

The summit is a rough uphill 2 kilometre hike northeast from the Alston-Teesdale road or you could yomp 20 kilometres around the skyline of the Burnhope Valley [NZ788375]

The summit of Burnhope Seat looking southeast

# 27

# Chopwell Woods

**Snaking through this area of mixed woodland and trying to hide within it, is an esker, a ridge of sand and gravel left by a river that once flowed in a tunnel beneath a thick ice sheet.**

Around 20,000 years ago ice from Scotland and Cumbria streamed through the Tyne valley into northeast England. About 15,000 years ago, as the climate started to warm, the ice began to melt more quickly and torrents of water flowed between the ice and the ground surface. These subglacial rivers carried debris that had been caught up in the ice and when this was deposited it left a sinuous ridge of sand and gravel running across the countryside. The esker in Chopwell Woods is around two kilometres long, 10 metres high and 50 metres wide and you can see the sand and rounded pebbles and cobbles in small scrapes on its sides. Eskers are just one of several features made of sand, gravel, silt and clay left by the melting ice sheet. Some, like eskers, deltas and outwash fans were deposited by flowing water while others, like moraine ridges and boulder clay (aka till or diamict) mostly melted directly out of the ice. Most tend to form characteristically hummocky terrain.

Chopwell Wood was here long before the conifers were planted and it is a designated as a Plantation on an Ancient Woodland Site (PAWS). Beneath the trees and the glacial deposits are coal seams, which have been exploited for centuries. Chopwell Colliery operated for 215 years before its closure in 1966. The settlement was regarded as dependent on the mine by planners so they labelled it as category 'D' meaning Chopwell village would be allowed to 'Decline'. Happily, in 1972 that label was rescinded and the village survives. The woodland is a popular amenity for walkers, cyclists, horse-riders and bird spotters.

The esker ridge is about 400 metres southeast of Chopwell Woods car park [NZ139581]

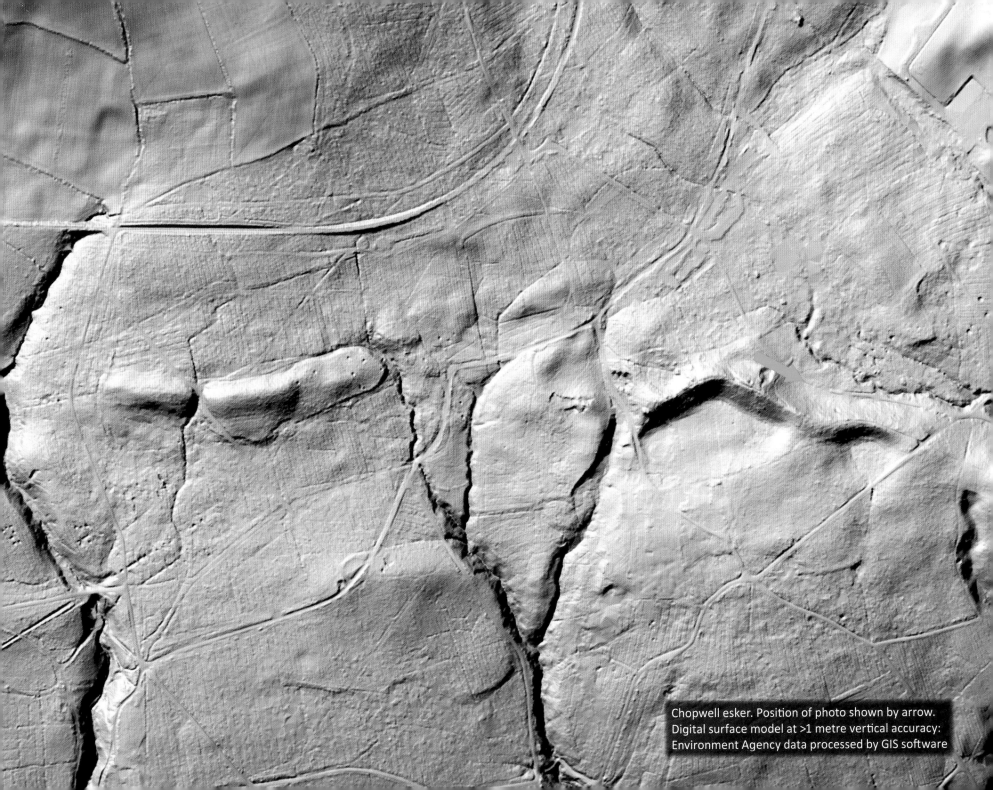

Chopwell esker. Position of photo shown by arrow.
Digital surface model at >1 metre vertical accuracy:
Environment Agency data processed by GIS software

# Coldberry Gutter

# 28

**High above Middleton-in-Teesdale there's a notch in the skyline, Coldberry Gutter, a Scheduled Ancient Monument. Until recently it was assumed to be a 'hush'.**

Hushes are a form of 'hydraulic mining' found all over the Pennine hills. Miners dammed up streams and then released the water to cut trenches exposing mineral veins. They and the many spoil heaps, shafts and old ruins are evidence of just how extensive the mining industry was here 100 years ago. Coldberry Gutter is around 20 metres deep and up to 100 metres across, cutting west-east across the watershed between the Bowlees and Hudeshope valleys for 1200 metres. It was thought to be an exceptionally large hush but earth scientists are now questioning that explanation for Coldberry Gutter and for other large hushes. The absence of significant mineral deposits in the trench, the type of rock in the walls (shale), the small volume of flood debris at the trench ends, plus doubts that the amount of water released was enough to excavate the trench, makes them think there is a more credible explanation: that the Gutter is largely natural - a glacial meltwater channel. The theory is that miners recognised they could make life easier by exploiting these natural excavations in the landscape by selective digging and then released dammed water to clear out debris.

But why is there a glacial meltwater channel here? During the last glaciation, 20,000 years ago, a thick ice sheet covered most of northern England including the high Pennines. That ice blocked all the pre-existing valleys and so meltwater ignored the old landscape and cut new escape channels. If you decide to explore the Gutter, there's a geological bonus. About 150 metres west of the watershed on the north slope a knob of harder rock sticks up. It's a piece of the Cleveland-Armathwaite dyke, a 60-million-year-old intrusion of dolerite from the Isle of Mull; the same rock that was quarried away at Cockfield Fell.

Take one of several footpaths north and east of Newbiggin. The Gutter is a 3 kilometre hike [NY931289]

Looking west down Coldberry Gutter

# 29

# Easington Colliery

**Perched precariously 30 metres above the sea in a cliff at Shippersea Bay is a little beach. But it's not a modern beach, it's a beach that is much older than the last Ice Age.**

To geologists it is famous, but it has also puzzled them. The beach is about 15 metres long and 2.5 metres thick and made of pebbles, cobbles, sand and shells. It sits on bedrock that has been burrowed into by marine animals and above it are more gravels and clays that were brought here by ice sheets that last covered northern England and the North Sea around 20,000 years ago. Earth scientists call this a 'raised beach'; a bit of perched ancient coastline that is evidence that sea level was once much higher than it is today. Exactly when the beach was formed has challenged scientists. They originally thought it was from a relatively warm period (an 'interglacial') about 125,000 years ago. Recent research using amino acid and luminescence analysis of the shells to estimate the age of the beach, suggests that it is from a much older interglacial period, around 220,000 years ago. Why it so high above present sea level is still being argued about.

The preservation of a piece of beach this old is rare and this is the most northerly interglacial beach in England. It probably survived because the rocky hill to the west protected it from erosion by later ice sheets. The years of research on this beach are far from academic, they are helping us understand when and how sea level falls and rises as ice sheets and the polar ice caps expand and shrink. These are matters that are only too relevant as we face the challenges of our changing climate.

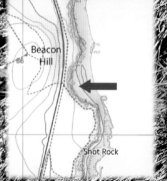

Beacon Hill
86

Shot Rock

Park at Easington Colliery and walk north along the coastal path for 1500 metres. The site is down a rough steep cliff path and not for the faint-hearted! [NZ442452]

The raised beach in the cliff at Shippersea Bay

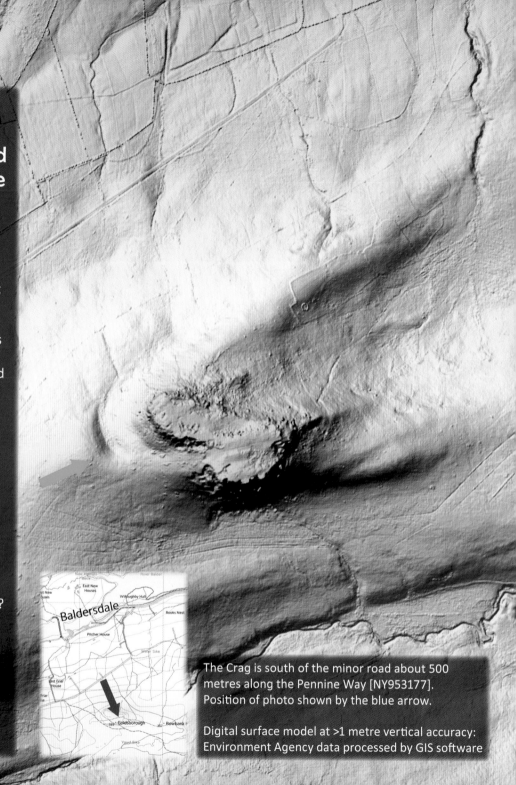

# Goldsborough

**The event that left the most profound mark on the Durham landscape was the Ice Age. The last ice sheet began to melt away around 15,000 years ago. But how do we know there was ice here and when it disappeared?**

Many places across the county provide the evidence but the hill at Goldsborough is special. From the west it looks like a table with a flat top and craggy north, west and south sides. It is made of a gritty Carboniferous sandstone and the sloping layers in the rock show that that 330 million years ago it was sand and grit in a fast-flowing river. But the spectacular sandy and pebbly layers and the fossilized pieces of tree roots you can find in the bedrock are not the reason it's in this book. Experts on the Quaternary period, the last 2.6 million years of Earth's history, identify Goldsborough as something called a 'crag and tail'; a rock hill and tapering ridge of debris created by an ice sheet as it scraped west to east down the valley. Goldsborough is unusual because it has two tails or 'horns'. This crag and tail and the nearby hummocks at Burners Hills are just two of a variety of humps and bumps in the landscape of Teesdale that tell us that a thick ice sheet streamed eastwards down from the Pennines and over Stainmore. Geologists call these features subglacial landforms and classify them as drumlins, roche moutonnées, lineations, etc, but in reality they all grade into each other and many have been re-moulded by different phases of ice movement. What they all prove is that an ice sheet perhaps 500 metres thick moved across the country streamlining the ground beneath.

How do scientists know that it melted away around 15,000 years ago? One piece of evidence comes from dating the first peat bogs that recolonized the area after the ice retreated. The ice left before these organic deposits started to form but the pollen they contain give us a minimum age of about 13,500 years. The second technique uses the effect of cosmic radiation on boulders moved by the ice to assess how long they have been at the Earth's surface. At Low Crags, a few kilometres down the valley, a date of 16,600 years ago was reported for the disappearance of the ice. To a geologist that's like yesterday!

The Crag is south of the minor road about 500 metres along the Pennine Way [NY953177]. Position of photo shown by the blue arrow.

Digital surface model at >1 metre vertical accuracy: Environment Agency data processed by GIS software

Goldsborough and its crags from the west

# 31

# Hartlepool Bay

Imagine, it's 7000 years ago. You're standing looking out over Hartlepool Bay, but instead of the grey North Sea there's green woodland and beyond that fenland and saltmarsh. Red deer forage in the glades and Stone Age hunters stalk them. Fact or fiction?

Fact! The last Ice Age and the subsequent melting had a profound effect on sea levels everywhere. Massive ice sheets locked up enormous quantities of the world's water, lowering global sea levels by as much as 120 metres below those today. The weight of ice had also depressed the land and so when the climate began to warm 15,000 years ago the release of ice pressure allowed the land to 'rebound' (called isostatic change). The melting of the ice discharged huge amounts of water into the seas and oceans, raising their level (eustatic change). These opposing changes didn't happen equally everywhere, nor did they happen at the same time. For geologists, geographers and archaeologists, sea level fluctuations and their consequences for landscapes and human history are a fertile area of research and are acutely relevant in the face of our changing climate.

But what is the hard evidence for these events and the forest and hunters in the Bay. Every few years, when the tide is very low, it reveals layers of peat and tree trunks. Found with them are pieces of worked flint, bones and antlers of deer. Submerged forests like these are often exposed around Britain's coast, in Northumberland and Cumbria and even dredged up in the middle of the North Sea. Analysis of pollen grains in these layers shows how the vegetation changed over time (from scrubby birch and alder, oak and elm, to grassland, fenland and saltmarsh). This sequence can be used in combination with radiocarbon ages to date the organic remains and sediments.

In 1972 there was a more spectacular find in the peat of the Bay. Human bones, including a skull, with worked flints near by. The bones have been dated at around 4600 years old, from the Neolithic or New Stone Age period. While this is an era defined by settling down and farming it seems our prehistoric ancestors continued, as we do today, to exploit the rich resources of our coastal environment.

The peat beds may be revealed along the Bay when there are very low tides [NZ519315]

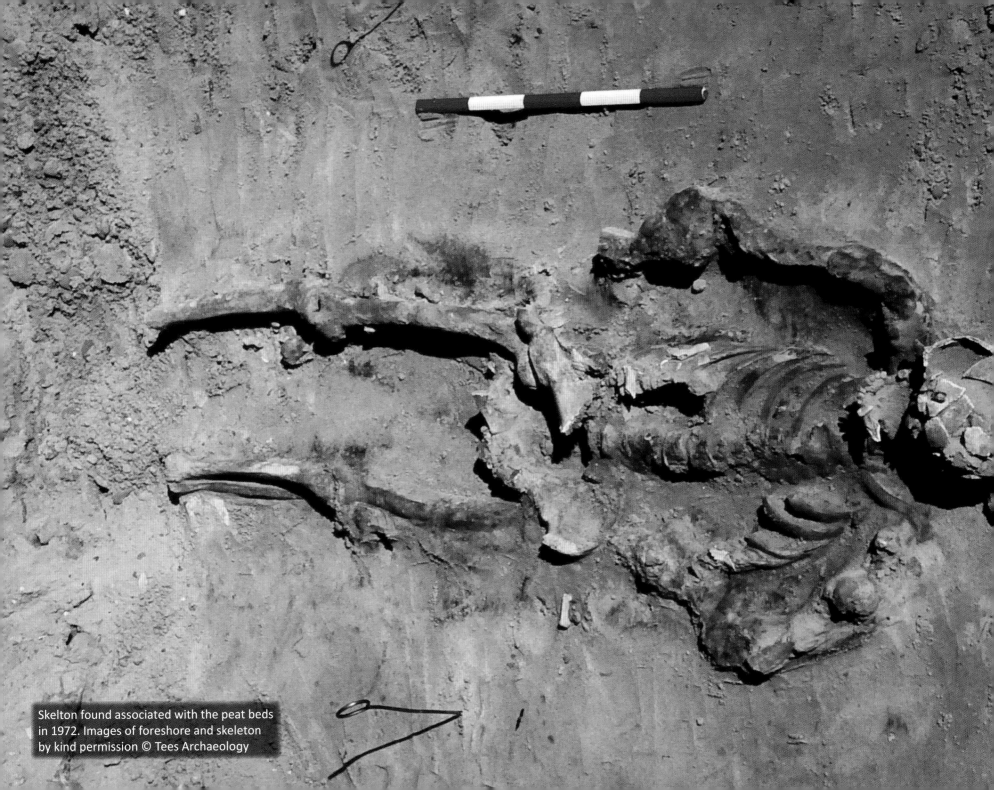

Skelton found associated with the peat beds in 1972. Images of foreshore and skeleton by kind permission © Tees Archaeology

# 32

# Moking Hurth Cave

Above the valley at Langdon Beck is a limestone scarp. At its base is a cave that connects a wealthy Quaker family, the bones of animals that no longer live in Britain, an enigmatic human skull and a cat from Shakespeare's Macbeth!

But first the rock. The cave (aka Malkins, Teesdale or Backhouse cave) is in a layer called the Great Limestone. 330 million years ago this rock began as limey mud and shell debris at the bottom of a tropical sea. While limestone may be hard, it is just impure calcium carbonate and so is slowly dissolved by rainwater which has absorbed carbon dioxide from the air and from organic material in the soil to become a weak acid. Limestone also has lots of cracks and joints that provide a pathway for the rainwater to join underground streams which dissolve the rock.

James Backhouse was a renowned naturalist. He and his father were from York, descendants of the Darlington Quaker banking family. In the 1880s they excavated the cave and discovered the bones of animals like wolf, bear, lynx, roe and red deer, wild pigs, sheep, and even capercaillie that had probably used the cave since the disappearance of the last ice sheet. There were also human bones, perhaps Bronze Age 2800-4000 years old. A young woman's skeleton and separate from the body was the skull, jammed into a rock crevice. Fragments of mandibles from two other individuals were also identified. Much of the cave entrance has since been quarried away and you will see a ruined limekiln nearby. The remaining narrow passages extend 300 metres into the hillside and are places for cavers, not for hikers like you and me to explore.

What of Shakespeare's cat? All caves have their folklore and given its grisly discoveries this one is no different; it was said to be the haunt of fairies and witches. Witches have 'familiars' and cats fill that role. In the opening scene of Macbeth one of the witches announces, 'I come Graymalkin'. In old English dialect a cat is a 'malkin', the origin of one of the cave's many names!

Park at Forest-in-Teesdale and walk north along the footpath for about 1.2 kilometres [NY867310]

Images of bones of bear and lynx courtesy of York Museums Trust https://yorkmuseumstrust. org.uk/ CC BY-SA 4.0. YORYM : 2005.449.1; YORYM : 2005.449.2

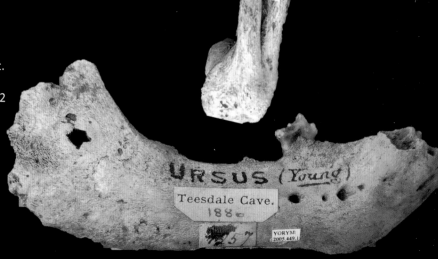

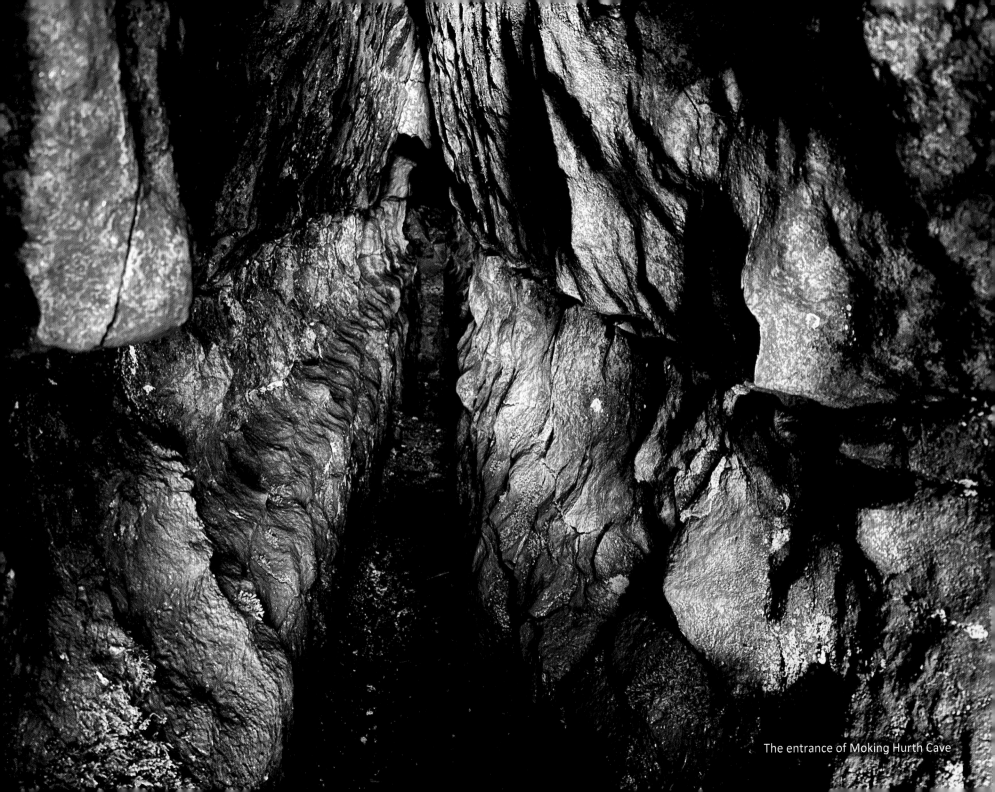

The entrance of Moking Hurth Cave

# Penshaw and Worm Hills

# 33

## This is a tale of two hills. They may share a 'worm' but they don't share rocks.

The song that everyone in the northeast knows will tell you that the Lambton Worm wrapped its tail seven times around Penshaw Hill. But this song was only written in 1867 and an earlier local myth claims it was Worm Hill, two kilometres away in Fatfield, that was squeezed. The rocks of Penshaw are much older than Worm Hill; around 260 million years old and from the Permian period. The rock is called the Raisby 'dolostone' and is a part of the Magnesian Limestone - it has more of the mineral magnesium. It was once sediment in a warm sea between 100 and 300 metres deep. The sea was called the Zechstein and while its west coast was only a couple of kilometres away, its east coast was hundreds of kilometres away in central Europe. Compared to rocks around it the Raisby dolostone is relatively hard and as a result millions of years of erosion have left it as a 30 – 60 metre high west facing scarp running south across Durham to Ferryhill. Penshaw Hill is part of that scarp.

Worm Hill's tale may be older, but its geology is a lot more recent. Geologists interpret it as a mound of sand and gravel that was deposited by meltwater from an ice sheet around 20,000 years ago. There are others who feel some or all of Worm Hill might have been constructed or moulded by our ancestors, but until someone excavates it the jury is out.

There are a few legendary worms in northeast England history. There's the Laidly Worm of Spindleston Heugh and the Sockburn Worm. If the artists' paintings are to be believed all these worms are more like dragons or serpents, the 'wyverns' which go back into Anglo-Saxon folklore. Lewis Carroll's Jabberwock was illustrated like this too – he wrote the poem while in the northeast and lived at Croft on Tees as a boy. Like many Victorians he was probably fascinated by these worms and the new science of geology that was discovering dragon-like dinosaurs in rocks around Britain.

You can park on the roadsides near to both hills and it's a short if steep walk up each. Penshaw [NZ333543]. Worm Hill [NZ310540]

Worm Hill at Fatfield

Penshaw Monument

# 34

# Piercebridge

**Mention geology and most people think volcanoes, earthquakes and dinosaurs. Sand and gravel will probably not get on the list. But they are still bits of rock and without them our lives would be pretty uncomfortable.**

The cement and concrete that builds our homes and infrastructure depends on them. Sand makes the glass in your windows, the abrasives in sandpaper and it's a constituent of bricks, paint and ceramics. Each of the valleys of the Tees, Tyne and Wear has ribbons of sand, gravel, silt and clay within and beneath them. Gaze at the deposits which form the floodplain and terraces of the River Tees from Piercebridge. These are sometimes in excess of 1500 metres wide and 10 metres thick. They were carried down by the river since the end of the last Ice Age 15,000 years ago, at first by huge amounts of meltwater as the ice sheets were retreating.

As well as being beautiful natural assets, rivers and their sediments have another, more menacing, relevance to us. In quieter times the river slowly shifts silt and sand along its bed, but when it floods the water easily moves cobbles and boulders too, something which happened often until Cow Green reservoir was built. Floods probably destroyed the first wooden Roman bridge which took Dere Street across the Tees and later unstoppable movements of the river channel meant parts of the second (stone) bridge were left as a causeway. Extreme weather events are forecast to become more common as the effects of climate change are felt and many river valleys across the country will experience increasingly frequent floods.

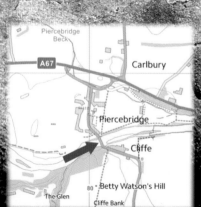

There is a car park to the east of the George Hotel. It is a short walk to the Roman Bridge remains [NZ210155]

ENGLISH HERITAGE

PIERCEBRIDGE

ROMAN BRIDGE

Piercebridge

# 35

# Ryhope cliffs

A short way off the cliffs at Ryhope is an isolated tower of rock. It hasn't got a name on the map but it's one of several towers along the coast. Geologists and geographers call them stacks.

At first glance it doesn't look like our coastline changes all that much, but ask a local and they will tell you that it has. There are the changes that we make, first dumping coal and industrial waste on the shore and now cleaning it up. But there are natural changes too, sometimes subtle, like the shifting of sand and shingle on beaches and sometimes dramatic, like the collapse of a cliff face. The anonymous stack at Ryhope is one of many clues about the way our rocky coastline is eroding; not so long ago it was part of the cliff. The cliff and the stack are Permian Magnesian Limestone, rocks which look solid enough but get close up and you will see many layers, faults and fissures. It is these weaknesses that the sea attacks. Stacks start as a bit of the cliff, wave action creates bays leaving a headland, sometimes a cave or arch develops behind the headland and eventually all that is left is the isolated tower. Ultimately that too will be washed away.

Because there is Magnesian Limestone from the mouth of the Tyne to Hartlepool the coastline is mostly one of bedrock cliffs. Further south on England's east coast, for example at Holderness or Norfolk, the coast is made of relatively soft clays from the Ice Age. These are eroding incredibly quickly, as a result of the increase in extreme weather and rising sea levels and so difficult and contentious decisions are being taken. It is no longer viewed as financially viable to defend every place under threat and entire neighbourhoods are being moved inland. Durham's coast is more stable, but it is still in retreat. That is why the A183 Coast Road was relocated and the whole coastline is regularly monitored for change. Nearby two stacks which still appear on maps (Jane Jiveson's Rock and Liddle Stacks) crumbled into the sea within the last seven years. Before 'Innominate Stack' does too you might want to go see it.

Take the footpath from Ryhope to join the England Coast Path at Halliwell Banks. Access to the foreshore is not easy [NZ416529]

Looking north from Ryhope to Sunderland

# 36

# Team Valley

**As you drive the A1 between Dunston and The Angel of the North have you ever wondered why Team Valley is as big as the Tyne and Wear valleys and yet the stream that runs in it is so small?**

Or wondered why the buildings on the Team Valley estate are low-rise lightweight structures, or even why the current £220 million upgrade to the A1 cost so much and required huge piling machines? It is a tale of ice sheets more than a kilometre thick and a glacial lake that covered an area that stretched almost from St James' Park, to the Stadium of Light, to The Riverside cricket ground. A contour map of the ground below Team Valley shows that bedrock is around 50 metres below the surface. It is an enormous buried valley cut between the valleys of the Tyne and Wear. Which way the valley flowed and whether it was cut by ice or water is still argued about. But there is agreement that there were two different massive ice sheets; one flowing eastwards down the Tyne Valley and the other southwards down the North Sea. Towards the end of the last Ice Age around 15,000 years ago, Tyne valley ice retreated westwards and meltwater was ponded up against the ice sheet in the North Sea. This created a lake which we call Glacial Lake Wear. Torrents of water full of gravel, sand, and mud flowed under and out of the melting ice sheets and into the lake. Away from the ice in deeper quieter waters the finer sediments were gently deposited. That mud and silt would become many metres of finely layered 'laminated' clays which now fill Team Valley.

After the ice left and the lake drained away the rivers Tyne and Wear cut their current courses to the sea and left the Team Valley occupied by a small stream - something that geographers, perhaps uncharitably, call a misfit. Laminated clays like these are unstable when wet and excavated, so buildings and bridges constructed on them need special preparation and engineering. This is the reason for the lightweight buildings and the expensive A1 upgrade. In the past structures which were not designed to deal with these clays have failed; so, when you are sitting in the traffic jams at Birtley you will be comforted to know that engineers and geologists today do talk to each other.

Laminated clay. Image by kind permission of C. Johnson/Roberts Environmental Ltd.

You can see Team Valley from the A1, or from a train travelling between Durham and Newcastle [NZ246594]

Looking northwest across Team Valley.
Image kindly taken by David Barnes

# 37

# Warren House Gill

**Walk the coastal path and you will cross several narrow, wooded valleys running eastwards to the sea: the Durham denes. While most suffered the ravages of many years of mining and heavy industry, today they are, with our help, returning to the natural havens they once were.**

The denes vary in size and some, like Castle Eden, extend for several kilometres west. But some valleys, called gills, are smaller. Warren House Gill is another enigmatic chapter of the Ice Age detective story that is the Durham coast – a clue about when and where the ice sheets that left their mark on the landscape and coastline came from. But first the denes and the gills, why are they here? Several of them, including Hawthorn, Crimdon, Castle Eden and Warren House follow the lines of deep old bedrock valleys that existed before the Ice Age and were plugged with its clay and stones. When the last ice sheet began to melt the streams in the denes once again flowed east cutting through the relatively soft glacial deposits. Sea level was initially a lot lower than it is today so these bedrock valleys continue deep under the present foreshore and beneath the floor of the North Sea.

The stony glacial clays and silts exposed in Warren House Gill are special because they go back to the early parts of the Ice Age, 300,000 – 500,000 years ago. They have been studied and argued over by geologists for more than 100 years. The oldest layers were originally thought to be boulder clay (or till) deposited under an ice sheet that had come from Scandinavia. The most recent research using modern analysis and dating concludes that an ice sheet from Scandinavia never made it onto present day land, and that the boulder clay is in fact clay, silt and stones that were smeared across bedrock by ice from Scotland and the North Sea. These conclusions not only re-write Durham's glacial story but are challenging the way scientists think about the Ice Age history of Britain. Now that's something to take your mind off the next up and down when you're hiking Durham's Heritage Coast!

You can take the footpath past the recycling site and sewage works down through the Gill [NZ445423]

Warren House Gill entrance on the foreshore with glacial clay, silt, sand and stones on either side

# 38

# Barningham

## South of Barnard Castle and close to the Durham – North Yorkshire boundary is Barningham Moor.

A thin and incomplete veneer of glacial clay and near- and far-travelled stones covers the bedrock - a series of repeating and almost horizontal layers of Carboniferous sandstone, shale and limestone. Several flat blocks of sandstone peep through the vegetation, these are detached pieces of bedrock, which probably haven't moved very far. But it's not the geology of these rocks that is significant here, it's the marks and carvings that cover their surfaces. Neolithic – Bronze Age rock art! While carved cups, rings and grooves are common and have been well documented in neighbouring Northumberland, there are few recorded in Durham and some of the more spectacular ones here were discovered less than 20 years ago. What these carvings mean is the subject of much debate amongst those with professional and amateur interests in pre-historic art. Lots of theories have been put forward from the sublime to the ridiculous. Many of the carvings are at the margins of uplands overlooking fertile ground below, others are close to ancient routes, some have been used in later circles and barrows. Some believe we may be missing the point in looking for meaning in the patterns, at least any meaning that 20th century society can comprehend and that they are part of a deeper spiritual relationship between ancient peoples and their landscape.

Rock art is one of many areas where geology and archaeology meet and there would undoubtedly be benefits in the two domains working together more. Many carvings are plainly made by human hand, while other rocks have unquestionably been shaped and sculpted by natural processes. But the origin of some marks on rocks is less clear. Were they caused by the scraping of ice sheets, or thousands of years of weathering of the natural layers and joints, or crafted by ancient people? Could it be that some are a combination of both. Perhaps to early societies the shapes created by nature were artforms too, something they may have chosen to imitate and augment?

Glacial erratic of Shap Granite

The moor is 3 kilometres southwest of Barningham village. The rock art is approximately 800 metres south of the minor road and 200 metres east of a track [NZ060084]

One of several rock art panels on Carboniferous sandstone blocks

# Blaydon Bank Quarry

# 39

**Close to the centre of Winlaton is an old quarry. 150 years ago this would have been just one of many quarries working the thick sandstones that form the high ground of Gateshead.**

These sandstones are around 315 million years old and from a part of the Carboniferous period called the Westphalian. The massive thick beds of rock in the lower part of the quarry face show channels that have been cut and then infilled with sand by a fast-flowing river. Near the top are thinner layers of sandstone and siltstone from gentle flows. Together they are evidence that these rocks were once sand in a large, southward flowing braided river. This river was much, much bigger than the Tyne or the Wear; think of the Brahmaputra in northeast India. We too were only a few degrees from the Equator back then.

Some parts of the sandstone walls show quarrymen's diagonal pick marks that were characteristic of that era. You can also see vertical 'half tubes'. These are boreholes that the workmen drilled to split the rock from the face. The quarry is recorded as supplying stone used to build houses on Blaydon Bank and in 1892, a Wesleyan school and chapel on Shibden Road. But it is also a place that a local character knew well. Lang Jack (John English or the Whickham Giant) measured six feet four inches and 20 stone and was said to be immensely strong. A stonemason by trade and an eccentric political figure, he built his own cottage near Fellside Road, Whickham and is said to have dragged the stone for it all the way from Blaydon Bank Quarry. Such was his fame that a likeness was sculpted in his honour and the monument now stands in Front Street, Whickham.

The quarry is adjacent to houses and beside the road [NZ180628]

The memorial to Lang Jack in Whickham

Fossilised channel in the sandstone of the old quarry

# 40

# Blaydon Burn

Entrance to Edward Pit and tar tunnel

Walk down Blaydon Burn today, and despite the scattered relics of mines and mills, so much vegetation has grown back that it is hard to believe that for two centuries the valley was completely filled with noisy and dirty industries.

The foundation for that industry began life in a tropical swamp around 315 million years ago. What were once primitive trees and mosses and the soil they grew in became coal and fireclay; rocks that are the basis of the heritage of this and many other parts of Durham. The coal and fireclay (aka seatearth or fossil soil) are, together with sandstones and mudstones, part of repeating cycles of rocks in the valley. The cycles are typical of Carboniferous Coal Measures strata and geologists call them cyclothems. They show that the original sediments were deposited in environments which changed frequently from rivers, to vegetated swamps, to lakes and sometimes brackish coastal waters.

While you will see many sandstone outcrops from the path, if you were to scramble and search around the steep sides of the valley, you will discover outcrops of the other rocks too, including a thick coal seam and its fossil soil, things which are rarely preserved. In and around the valley you will also get glimpses of the remains of the industries they spawned: drift mines in the valley sides, the fire-brick factory, the coke and tar works and the rail lines that serviced them all.

Today Blaydon Burn is a place where nature is recovering and you can see dippers and yellow wagtails in the stream, green woodpeckers and tawny owls in the woods, not to mention a whole variety of insects and plants, some of which are tolerant of soils contaminated by past industries. There is not a little irony in the fact that the dirty raw materials that were exploited in the valley were themselves once a part of nature.

You can access the Dene from the south, north and Beweshill Lane [NZ170625]

A thick coal seam on the side of Blaydon Dene

# 41

# Consett

**Until 1980 when you drove south on the A68 into the Derwent Valley you would often see a big red glow in the sky above Consett.**

Gaze southeast from the A68 now and you will see no glow or dust, nor any sign of the huge steel and ironworks that produced them, just a reclaimed green hillside and retail park. The industry was founded on local coal, iron ore and limestone. Around 320 million years ago these rich resources were peaty swamps, muddy lagoons and coral seas. Exactly how the iron ores formed has been the subject of a long geological debate. Was it through iron minerals being deposited with the mud and silt, or iron-rich fluids percolating through the rocks after deposition? Did microbes have something to do with it. Maybe it was a combination of all these things?  But the outcome, after millions of years of compaction, were shales containing layers and nodules of an ore called siderite (iron carbonate: $FeCO_3$). The more persistent and richer seams had distinctive names: the Ten Bands Ironstone, the No. 1 Ironstone and the German Bands Ironstone; perhaps named after the 17th century German sword makers of Shotley Bridge.

Before 1841 Consett was less than 40 scattered houses and the total population was 139. Then the Derwent Iron Company was established and by 1854 the population had grown to 20,000. The reserves of local ore proved to be small and were of poor quality and so supplies were transported from the Cleveland Hills and from Sweden. 43 years ago production ended. Depending on your viewpoint the cause was economic or political. Consett went through tough times after the closure of the steelworks and unemployment peaked at three times the national average. The town is a very different place now, retail parks and light industry have replaced a plant that once employed 6000 people. Consett's story is one that is seen in many places that have depended on the exploitation of natural resources, whether they be iron ore, lead and coal, and now, maybe, oil and gas.

The steelworks site has been totally reclaimed. Walk along the old rail line, now the Waskerley Way [NZ099494] or along the River Derwent to the old ironworks at Allensford [NZ080503]

Ironstone nodules

# 42

# Dinsdale

**What connects the man who played a key role in creating the nation of Canada, smelly baths loved by Georgians and Victorians, Durham Jail and subsiding ground in Darlington?**

The answer is gypsum, hydrated calcium sulphate, $CaSO_4.2H_2O$, deposited between layers of mud in a shallow sea that evaporated frequently in the arid climate of the Permian period 250 million years ago. In 1789 workmen employed by John Lambton were boring a hole in search of coal on the bank of the Tees just west of Middleton One Row. After 22 metres of red rock they were shocked to find warmish water that smelled of rotten eggs gushing from the hole. The workmen claimed the water cured their rheumatism and skin complaints. Medical men of the time confirmed the health benefits of these sulphur-rich waters and by 1797 a bath house had been built to compete with spas at Croft and Harrogate. People would come not only to bathe in the water but to drink it too and soon more accommodation was needed. Dinsdale Spa Hotel was built in 1829 by the grandson of John Lambton, none other than John George Lambton, 1st Earl of Durham and Governor General of British North America. He was often known as Radical Jack and in Canada as Lord Durham. He is renowned for his contribution to the establishment of their country and the assimilation of the French Canadians. Sadly, the Dinsdale mansion, designed by architect Ignatius Bonomi who also built the first bridge on the Stockton to Darlington Railway and Durham Jail, didn't generate enough business and was sold on in 1844.

The link between the spa and subsiding ground? Circulating groundwater dissolves the highly soluble gypsum producing sulphate-rich (spa) water and hydrogen sulphide causing the rotten egg smell. When the gypsum dissolves the rocks above cave in, and that can cause subsidence at the ground surface and sometimes damage to buildings and infrastructure. The gypsum layers under Dinsdale also lie beneath Darlington and Croft. Back to health and something that is genuinely beneficial; a walk along the Teesdale Way beside the river, past the old spa and through the peaceful scenery of this part of the Tees valley.

Footpaths, including the Teesdale Way, run past the old bath house (pictured) west of Middleton One Row [NZ343120]

Dinsdale Spa, Durham: people gathered at the riverside.
Line engraving by S. Lacey, 1833, after T. Allom: Public
Domain. Inset: Dinsdale Bath House c1905

# 43

# Durham Cathedral

**Is there an English cathedral with a more dramatic location? Or one with such a wonderful symmetry between the building and the bedrock it stands on?**

Directly beneath the Cathedral walls and pillars is solid sandstone bedrock; there was no need of a manmade foundation. Much of the building is constructed of the same sandstone, quarried less than 500 metres away across the river. The rock is called the Low Main Post, a Carboniferous sandstone that 315 million years before was sand in a river delta. The sandstone takes its name from the coal seam below it and provided a strong roof for those mining the coal across the Durham and Northumberland. But beneath the Cathedral this coal seam remains intact as subsidence beneath their mother church was not something even coal-owning Bishops would countenance. You can see the natural sandstone in the cliffs beside the river and the way the layers in it here and in the Cathedral's stone blocks slope at a variety of angles; recording their origin as river sands. The Low Main Post was strong, but it was not a stone that could be finely carved and so the pillars and arches are simple but strikingly bold. While sandstone dominates there are many other different stones in the church. Some are local like the columns and slabs of black fossiliferous Frosterley 'Marble', a Carboniferous limestone from Weardale. There are Carboniferous stones from the south of the county too: Bede's tomb is 'marble' (limestone) from Egglestone and 20th century external building repairs used sandstone from Barnard Castle. Other stones are more exotic, pale limestones from Purbeck, alabaster from the Midlands, the Neville Screen of Jurassic limestone from Caen and the imported serpentines, marbles and lapiz lazuli inlays of the incongruous Victorian pulpit.

The river gorge and meander that creates the peninsula and give the Cathedral and castle their dominance over the City of Durham are many millions of years younger than the sandstone they cut through. They were cut by huge amounts of meltwater rushing down the valley as the last ice sheet melted less than 15,000 years ago. The river is a lot more peaceful today. Take the path beside it and then head up the winding street to the Cathedral and you will be walking up the same road people used to haul the stone from the quarry to build the Cathedral almost 900 years ago.

The cathedral is a short uphill walk from bus and train services [NZ273420]

Durham Cathedral and the Old Fulling Mill
from the south bank of the River Wear

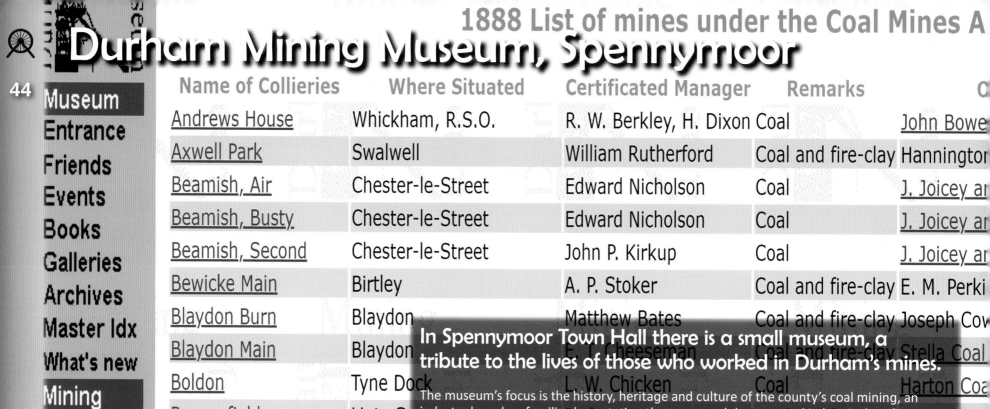

# Durham Mining Museum, Spennymoor

# 44

**1888 List of mines under the Coal Mines A**

| Name of Collieries | Where Situated | Certificated Manager | Remarks | O |
|---|---|---|---|---|
| Andrews House | Whickham, R.S.O. | R. W. Berkley, H. Dixon | Coal | John Bowe |
| Axwell Park | Swalwell | William Rutherford | Coal and fire-clay | Hanningtor |
| Beamish, Air | Chester-le-Street | Edward Nicholson | Coal | J. Joicey ar |
| Beamish, Busty | Chester-le-Street | Edward Nicholson | Coal | J. Joicey ar |
| Beamish, Second | Chester-le-Street | John P. Kirkup | Coal | J. Joicey ar |
| Bewicke Main | Birtley | A. P. Stoker | Coal and fire-clay | E. M. Perki |
| Blaydon Burn | Blaydon | Matthew Bates | Coal and fire-clay | Joseph Cov |
| Blaydon Main | Blaydon | E. T. Cheeseman | Coal and fire-clay | Stella Coal |
| Boldon | Tyne Dock | L. W. Chicken | Coal | Harton Coa |
| Burnopfield | Lintz Green | Rodger Mason | | John Bowe |
| Byermoor | Burnopfield | J. P. Duman | Coal and fire-clay | John Bowe |
| Deckham Hall | Gateshead | J. Scott Laing | Coal | Upper a |
| Dipton | Lintz Green | R. Mitchinson | | John Bowe |
| East Castle | Lintz Green | J. Swallow | Coal | East Castle |
| East Pont | Green | J. Swallow | Coal | East Pontop |
| East Tanf | Green | | | Joicey ar |
| Felling | shea | William Lee | | John Bowe |
| Garesfiel | lands | Matthew Bates | Coal and fire-clay | Joseph Cov |
| Garesfiel | Green | R. Oliver | | Marquis of |
| Greenside | n | W. Rochester | Coal. Landsale | R. Simpson |
| Hamsterley | Ebchester | William Allen | Coal and fire-clay | H. W. Wats |

In Spennymoor Town Hall, free parking behind it [NZ257338]

In Spennymoor Town Hall there is a small museum, a tribute to the lives of those who worked in Durham's mines.

The museum's focus is the history, heritage and culture of the county's coal mining, an industry based on fossilized vegetation that grew and decomposed in hot Carboniferous swamps around 320 million years ago. Extending beyond the county into northern England and to mining in general, the museum has exhibits that show life underground, the equipment used and many photographs and documents. But perhaps the hidden treasure is the web site. It may be dated in design, but it is functional, maintained and rich in content, with over 100,000 records relating to northern mining. While the definitive mine plans are held by the Coal Authority in Mansfield, the data in this local and voluntary institution are remarkable; there is information about each mine, its location, annual production figures, colliery personnel, mine plans, newspaper articles and more.

The content is eclectic, but perhaps the most poignant are the records of the deaths in mines: a database simply called 'In Memoriam'. Names, dates, pit, cause of death and mines inspectors' and inquest reports are all respectfully maintained. Quite unexpectedly, I came across a personal connection in the Museum's archive of newspaper reports recording the death and inquest of my great-great-grandfather, John Jackson, a hewer, killed in a roof fall in Ellenborough Colliery, Maryport in 1853. He was just one of more than 100,000 men, women and children killed in coal mines in Britain since the 18th century. The figure does not include the many more who subsequently died of illnesses caused by dust and injury. At the peak of coal mining over 165,000 people worked in over 300 pits in Durham. If you would like to experience what it is like to go down a coal mine or how mining families lived, head to Beamish Museum which is only 30 minutes away.

**Website navigation menu:** Museum · Entrance · Friends · Events · Books · Galleries · Archives · Master Idx · What's new · Mining · History · Mines . . . · Main · UK Mines · Shafts · Borings · Mines List · Managers · Abandon · Coll. Maps · Company · Who's Who · Minera

Items in Durham Mining Museum

# 45

# Felling

There have been many heartbreaking tragedies caused by explosions in coal mines in Durham. On 25th May, 1812 at Felling Colliery 92 lives were lost. It was a turning point in mine safety across Britain and the world.

First opened in 1779, Felling Colliery had two shafts, John and William, which had been newly deepened to 172 metres to work a 90-centimetre-thick coal called the Low Main. Like most collieries at this time, coal was mined by driving corridors (stalls) leaving a grid of pillars to support the roof. To prevent dangerous gases building up, the workings were ventilated by burning a fire at the bottom of one shaft (the upcast) and drawing air down the downcast shaft via a one-way system through the mine, using a series of doors. Coal and the black coaly shales that occur with it, naturally contain several gases from decomposing organic material. Miners knew the gases well and had their own terms for each. There was firedamp (methane: explosive), whitedamp (carbon dioxide: toxic), blackdamp or choakdamp (carbon monoxide: explosive and toxic), stinkdamp (hydrogen sulphide: explosive and toxic) and afterdamp (the mixture of dangerous gases left after an explosion).

At 11:30am on 25th May, 1812 there was an explosion so powerful that it blew the winding gear from the top of both shafts. The cause was believed to be firedamp. Thick coal dust settled almost three kilometres down wind. 92 men and boys perished in the explosion. The youngest was eight-year-old Thomas Gordon, a 'trapper', paid 9d (about 4p) for a 12-hour day to open and close the doors that controlled the circulating air. Thomas' name and those of 90 others are inscribed on a modest memorial in St Mary's churchyard nearby. It was the local vicar, Reverend John Hodgson, who raised public awareness of the need to improve mine safety. His campaigning resulted in meetings of doctors, clergy, mine owners and engineers. One member was William Reid Clanny, a Sunderland doctor who had devised the first, but impractical, safety lamp. Another was George Stephenson, who invented the Geordie lamp, a rival to the Davy lamp that was ultimately used in mines across the world.

The low tower capping John Pit shaft is on waste ground. It can be seen from a nearby footpath [NZ273622]. The memorial is at the entrance to the St Mary's churchyard [NZ286619]

Merged old and new views of John Pit, Felling

# 46

# Groverake Mine

**Standing tall at the head of the valley of the Rookhope Burn is the headgear of one of the last fluorite mines in Durham. As a memorial to north Pennine mining, Groverake's winding frame is every bit the equal of any commissioned art installation.**

Fluorite (fluorspar to miners and most others) is the mineral form of calcium fluoride, $CaF_2$. In the rocks at Groverake and at many other places in the northern Pennines, it occurs in veins, together with lead, iron and zinc ores (galena, siderite and sphalerite), quartz and many other minerals. They crystallised out of hot mineral-rich fluids which permeated the rocks and particularly favoured cracks and dislocations caused by geological faults. Until a few years ago, the origin of these fluids was thought to be the 400-million-year-old Weardale Granite (never seen at surface but proved in a borehole at Rookhope). Now they are believed to be related to the intrusion of the Whin Sill 295 million years ago.

There has been mining at Groverake for centuries. The Beaumont Company initially extracted lead but in 1897 switched to mining the thick veins of fluorspar for use as a flux for iron and steel production and also for the chemical industry. British Steel took over in the mid-20th century and greatly expanded and deepened the mine, but ultimately in the face of cheap foreign imports it proved uneconomic and ceased operating in 1999. The European Commission regards fluorspar as a Critical Raw Material and is concerned about its reliance on imported sources; China accounts for around 60% of world supply and Mexico is also a substantial producer. Meanwhile, a small mine is now operating in an old limestone quarry at Frosterley in Weardale, but its output is not industrial, it is beautiful green and blue/purple fluorite crystals for sale to mineral collectors.

Just south of and clearly visible from the Rookhope-Allenheads road [NY894441]

Fluorite with calcite from the Diana Maria mine, Weardale. Image courtesy of Crystal Classics Ltd

# 47

# Killhope

**There are many places in Durham that illustrate aspects of lead mining and the lives of those who worked in them. Killhope Museum, at the head of Weardale, is the perfect place to tell their story.**

How and where lead was formed and its relationship with rocks has been described elsewhere in this book. These pages are more about life in the remote northern Pennine hills that were the centre of lead mining in Britain 150 years ago. Killhope, like similar mines in adjacent Northumberland and Cumbrian valleys, is almost 500 metres above sea level; a place with a harsh climate and impoverished soils. The lead ore found in veins that criss-crossed these hills had been mined for centuries and made a select few families incredibly rich. For others, the majority, life could be punishingly hard. These were the miner-farmers, working in the mines but also needing to eke out a living on isolated steadings with a small house, barn and a few animals. Many dot the hillsides today. Despite the philanthropy of some mine companies, the vagaries of the lead mining industry and the hazardous conditions underground meant miner-farmers were no strangers to poverty and ill-health; large families and high rates of child mortality were constants. Some chose to look for a better life elsewhere and emigrated to North America and to Australia. At Killhope you can read the letters these families exchanged in the 1850s; they are disarmingly factual and poignant. People in these upland areas were not embraced by an Anglican church focused on its softer valley parishes below. They were converted by Wesley to Methodism and when this faith lost its missionary zeal, became Primitive Methodists. Visit the area and you will see many examples of the chapels and schools they built, some with their original internal architecture and furniture.

Killhope mine opened in 1853 and closed around 1910. Restoration began in 1980 and today you can experience a trip into the mine, see the washing floor and crushing mill and waterwheel where the ore (galena) was processed (dressed) before it went for smelting. But perhaps most evocative are the stories of the daily lives of the people who lived and worked high in the Pennine Hills 150 years ago.

Museum is close to the county border on the A689 [NY825430]

....He has a stirck and a calf And he has a good crop of lambs and he has the land in very good trim. In fact he is doing very well with Farming. Well Brother a man in this Countery has to be very skillful about Farming for you have nearly duble as much rent to pay every year as you can make of them. And you may depend upont that we have very hard times. Stock is as high as it was in the last letter I sent you and flour has rised to 3s per stone, mutton is 7d per lb Beef about the same. Potates is 8d per stone. Bacon is about 10d per lb and in fact it is the hardest times that I ever so in my life time. But thair was the best pays in this Countery the last year that has been for a long time which was a great Blessen to all the Countery…..

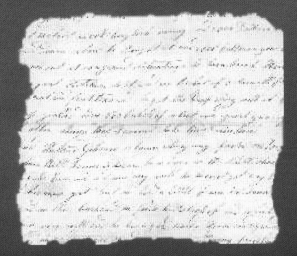

....For after given birth to her tenth Child which is a fine litel girl and is in very good hielth and all of them is in very good hielth at presant and is dowing very well but it is the greatest misfortune that ever came to Thomas Millburn and the greatest loss that ever came to his Familey. Tow of the Children you know died long before you left home and Eight is livn yet. When gave birth to the Child on the 9th of January and she got very good maens until the 23th. We all thought she was getin the best means she has don for a long time But she has been subject to swollen legs when baring child and her leg never got beter this time as it ought to have don and the Black Erysipelus took place and the Doctor never could stop it progress which soon ended in Mortefication and death…..

A ruined small holding in the north Pennines and extracts from letters written to relatives who had emigrated to the USA around the 1850s. Extracts by kind permission of Killhope Lead Mining Museum

# Saltholme

# 48

**Without the rocks that hide deep beneath the ground surface Teesside would be a very different place.**

The heavily industrialised land to the north of the Tees estuary is covered by a veneer of manmade fill which sits on soft tidal deposits of sand, silt and mud and glacial clays. Beneath those are 240-million-year-old sandstones and mudstones, and deep below those are limestones that contain thick layers of anhydrite and halite. 255 million years ago these minerals were salts in a warm sea that extended from Durham to Warsaw. The level and extent of this primeval sea - called the Zechstein - fluctuated regularly and so the environment changed from open seas 300 metres deep, to reefs and shallow coastal lagoons, to desert plains and back again. It was the evaporation of highly saline water at the western margin of that ancient sea that produced the layers of salts deep below Teesside and all along the Durham coast.

Anhydrite (calcium sulphate, $CaSO_4$) contains 24% sulphur, a mineral crucial in the manufacture of chemicals and fertilizer. In 1926 Imperial Chemical Industries (ICI) opened a mine at Billingham to extract it. The shaft was 260 metres deep and the mine ultimately excavated around 320 kilometres of galleries and roadways. The mine closed in 1978 but extensive underground chambers remain attracting controversial proposals for the storage of waste including low level nuclear material and fly ash. A little further east, about 350 metres beneath Greatham, Saltholme and Port Clarence, are the deposits of halite, (common salt - sodium chloride, $NaCl$). They were originally extracted by 'uncontrolled' brine pumping, but that caused subsidence at the ground surface. Controlled brine pumping was introduced but in places that brought problems of salt contamination of groundwater resources in overlying rocks. Brine pumping moved deeper and further east towards Seal Sands and used better methods of extraction. Since the 1950s some of the cavities created have been used to store gases including methane, nitrogen and hydrogen. Today cavities within the salt for natural gas storage are specially designed and engineered.

There's both irony and symmetry that it was a prehistoric natural sea, that brought the industry, that caused the subsidence and enlarged wetlands, that today give a home to wildlife. Visit RSPB's wonderful Saltholme reserve, enjoy the birds and perhaps reflect on the ancient environments beneath.

There are several walks and places to view the subsidence (and birds) at RSPB Saltholme [NZ502231]

Anhydrite workings beneath Billingham.
Image courtesy of Stockton Picture
Archive – Stockton-on-Tees Libraries

# 49

# South Shields

**Have you ever wondered why there are a lot of flint pebbles and sometimes lumps of chalk on the foreshore at the mouth of the Tyne and adjacent beaches?**

Flint and chalk bedrock are common in the southeast of England but on land only extend as far north as Flamborough Head. So why are these stones here? The chief reason is the coal trade. For centuries, ships carrying coal from the northeast of England to London would return to the Tyne full of sand and flint and chalk gravel dredged from the River Thames. The material was needed as ballast to ensure the ships stayed stable at sea. Once they arrived, they dumped their load in the river to take on coal. But that started to obstruct ships so ballast docks and staithes sprang up to offload the sand and gravel ashore. The coal trade was exceedingly profitable and the ballast business became the centre of political and legal battles. On one side was the protectionism of the burgesses of Newcastle, on the other the financial ambitions of those excluded from that monopoly - including the bishops of Durham.

The ballast piles got bigger and spread along the shoreline, so waggonways and then railways were built to create piles further from the river and along the coast. South Shields came to be dominated by huge hills of flint gravel and sand that spread across the east of the town. But it wasn't only ballast that was dumped in South Shields. Cheap and plentiful coal and nearby seawater meant there had been a flourishing salt-making trade along the riverside since the 15th century and later that would spawn chemical industries. Bottle and glass manufacturing sprang up in the 17th century too. All these trades generated waste and that waste ended up as huge piles within the town. Throughout the 19th and 20th centuries most of these ballast and waste hills were progressively cleared, sometimes by 'relief labour' in times of economic depression. Some sites were restored to green spaces, like the Marine parks, and today it is hard to appreciate what was once there.

Salem Street is approximately where Thames Street used to be [NZ362673]

Flint and chalk gravel on the bank of the River Tyne

Ballast hill north of Thames Street, South Shields in 1940s and today. Old image by kind permission of South Tyneside Libraries

# 50

# Stony Heap

**This small valley beside a former coal mine is one of many places across Durham where vivid orange deposits used to coat the stream bed.**

Discharges of water from coal mines have posed a pollution problem for years. Coal-bearing rocks slope gently beneath eastern Durham and extend far below the North Sea. From at least the 14th century miners have excavated pits, shafts and passageways to exploit the coal, creating an underground labyrinth. Most of these mines were 'wet', and in order to work the coal, groundwater had to be continuously pumped away; when mining ended those pumps were turned off. Water flowed back in, flooding a complex and often unknown system of partially collapsed workings, dissolving iron which occurs naturally in the coal and shale that remained. In some places the rising levels of acidic, iron-rich, mine water threatens aquifers (rocks used as underground sources of drinking water). In other places it reaches the surface and discharges into streams and rivers. Then the iron in the water oxidises and blankets the river bed with ochre. Water from opencast workings, mine spoil heaps and natural drainage through similar rocks contributes to the problem. The impact on wildlife can be severe, in particular on fish and invertebrates. But there are also economic and social downsides affecting amenity and property values.

The legal position is that no one can be held liable for pollution from the majority of mines in the UK and it is only since 1999 that a mine operator has had any obligation to deal with such issues. Nonetheless, mine water discharges represent a significant pollution threat and the Environment Agency and the Coal Authority are tasked with mitigating the more serious pollution risks. Stony Heap is one of many 'passive' treatment plants that use aeration, lagoons and reedbeds to clean the water. But when the risk of pollution is severe, such as at Dawdon, where it threatened an aquifer supplying water to 20% of the population, a sophisticated filtration process using industrial chemicals was built. Dawdon is also an example of a more positive and innovative 21st century use of the water in abandoned mines: providing geothermal heat for homes and industry.

There is parking space beside the gates of the site and a footpath leads around the reed beds [NZ147514]

Stony Heap mine water treatment site

# Endnote

Seek out the special places and you will find Durham's landscapes - the Pennine moors and dales, its wooded valleys and its rocky coastline - will give as much pleasure as the mountains, lakes, escarpments and beaches of its northern neighbours. Durham residents know it also has an advantage; most of its treasures are unknown to the madding crowds. Add to that natural mix a cultural and mining heritage that is second to none and you have a region that deserves exploration. I hope this book inspires you to do just that and you visit places that you may not know as well as see new things in places you know well. Of course I hope this book will reinforce that, as elsewhere, it is Durham's rocks that underpin this wonderful diversity.

Those of us who live here and those who return year after year to visit will tell you passionately that England's three most northern counties are the natural jewels in the nation's crown. Northumberland, Cumbria and Durham are also the only counties I felt I knew well enough to be comfortable writing books about. So this is an endnote in more ways than one and Durham will be the last of the 'county Rocks books' I write. But rocks have an influence on other things in the north so maybe......

Upper Teesdale

# Links to resources

Open the camera app on your phone and point at the QR code

Durham
Wildlife Trust

www.durhamwt.com

Durham County
Council

www.durham.gov.uk

Durham Mining
Museum

www.dmm.org.uk

Northeast
Geological Society

www.negs.org.uk

Geological
Society of UK

www.geolsoc.org.uk

British Geological Survey

https://webapps.bgs.ac.uk/
Memoirs/docs/B06817.html

www.bgs.ac.uk
*search*
*Geology Viewer*

www.bgs.ac.uk
*search*
*GeoIndex (onshore)*

Dunston Staithes

# The author

Ian Jackson was born and raised in Carlisle. His love of rocks began in the late 1950s in the Lake District fells. He has a degree in geology and geography from the University of Newcastle upon Tyne and is a Chartered Geologist and Fellow of the Geological Society.

Ian spent 18 years surveying the geology of parts of the north of England, for the British Geological Survey. Later he was responsible for national and international programmes that produced the first UK, European and global digital geological maps and made them web accessible.

Ian retired from the position of BGS Operations Director in 2011 and moved to Bardon Mill in Northumberland. He hikes in northern England every week, often leading guided walks and giving talks. In addition to many scientific maps, articles and reports, he is the author of Britain Beneath Our Feet, an atlas of the UK's geology and Northumberland Rocks and Cumbria Rocks, sister publications to this book.

**Durham**
Wildlife Trust
**From Tees to Tyne**

Durham Wildlife Trust is a charity and was established in 1971. We operate from Tyne to Tees and are part of the federation of 46 charities across the U.K. that together form the Wildlife Trusts. Recognised by their badger logo, each individual Wildlife Trust is an independent organisation conserving wildlife in its local area.

Our Trust was founded by dedicated volunteers with a passion to conserve their local wildlife. We act locally but make a difference nationally to restore the natural environment by being advocates for wildlife and influencing local and national government and wider society.

We have the backing of members, supporters and partners and through our projects and reserves provide opportunities for participation, education and enhanced wellbeing.

Our prime goal in this decade is to deliver species and habitat restoration projects across land and sea. To do that we seek to maximise our effectiveness by operating at the largest possible scale and achieve 30% of land for wildlife by 2030.